THIS BOOK BELONGS TO

Jesus rides into Jerusalem

STORIES FROM THE NEW TESTAMENT

STORIES FROM

THE

NEW TESTAMENT

Geddes & Grosset

ISBN 1 85534 560 9

Printed and bound in Slovenia

10 9 8 7 6 5 4 3 2

CONTENTS

THE CHRISTMAS STORY   9
  Mary of Nazareth   9
  Mary and Joseph Go on a Journey   12
  The Angel and the Shepherds   15
  The Visit of the Wise Men   19
  Jesus of Nazareth   25
  Jesus Chooses His Friends   30

JESUS THE MERCIFUL   35
  One Sabbath Day   35
  The Soldier's Servant   38
  The Widow's Son   41
  Storm-Tossed   43
  The Man with Four Friends   47
  Little Talitha   49
  The Boy with the Loaves and Fishes   53
  The Lord of the Sabbath   57

THE GREAT TEACHER   61
  Teacher and Friend   61
  The Lost Sheep   65
  The Boy who went Astray   68
  The Story of Zacchaeus   72
  The Grateful Heart   75
  Jesus and the Children   77
  The Blind Beggarman   79

In Bethany 81
Jesus Rides into Jerusalem 83

THE SAVIOUR OF THE WORLD 87
Jesus in Jerusalem 87
The Last Meal Together 89
In the Garden 91
In the Palace 94
Jesus before Pilate 96
On a Hill called Calvary 100
The First Easter Day 102

UNTO ALL NATIONS 109
A New Beginning 109
At the Gate Beautiful 112
Stephen, the Faithful 115
Philip and the Stranger 119
Peter and Eneas 122
The Lady of Kindness 124
The Rescue of Peter 126

PAUL THE TRAVELLER 131
A Boy in Tarsus 131
The Great Awakening 133
In Peril by the Heathen 138
In Peril in Philippi 142
Preaching in Athens 146
In Peril in Ephesus 151
In Peril from his Countrymen 153
In Peril on the Sea 155

LIST OF PLATES

Facing page

THE SHEPHERDS KNELT BEFORE THE TINY BABE   16

THE VISIT OF THE WISE MEN   17

THE GOOD SAMARITAN   64

HIS FATHER'S LOVING EYES RECOGNIZED HIM   65

JESUS RIDES INTO JERUSALEM   *96 and frontispiece*

JESUS BEFORE PILATE   97

JESUS APPEARS TO MARY MAGDALENE   112

STEPHEN PRAYED, "LORD JESUS RECEIVE MY SPIRIT."   113

THE LADY OF KINDNESS   128

THE RESCUE OF PETER   129

THE ROMAN SOLDIERS TAKE PAUL BY NIGHT FROM JERUSALEM   144

PAUL TELLS HIS FELLOW PASSENGERS OF HIS VISION   145

THE CHRISTMAS STORY

Mary of Nazareth

Far away in the Eastern land of Palestine, there is a little country town of white houses, called Nazareth. Nazareth lies high up among the hills of Galilee. Hills are all round it, and on the hillside are olive groves, vineyards, fig trees, and tall cypresses. And when springtime comes the fields are filled with flowers, glowing with lovely colour against the grey rocks and the green olive trees.

Long long ago, almost two thousand years ago, there lived in that same little town of Nazareth, a maiden called Mary. Mary had grown up in Nazareth, and she loved it. As a child she had gone in spring with the other children to gather the lovely wild flowers. She knew all the folk of the countryside: the women fetching water from the well, the shepherds minding their sheep, the farmers sowing and reaping, the fishermen who spread their nets in the blue sea of Galilee. She saw the travellers passing on the great trade road from Damascus to distant Egypt, saw the camel trains carrying goods; and very often she saw companies of soldiers in armour, Roman soldiers, marching along the roads, their tramping feet sending up clouds of dirt, their helmets flashing in the sunshine.

Every Sabbath Mary went with her parents and friends to worship God in the synagogue, which was what Mary's church was called. Mary heard all those stories which we read in the Old Testament, and which are really the history of Mary's own people, the Jews. She heard of Abraham and Isaac, of Jacob and Joseph, of Moses the great leader, of Ruth and Queen Esther, of King David and Solomon.

Now Mary was grown-up, and she was to marry kind Joseph, the carpenter, who also lived in Nazareth. Joseph was older than Mary, but they loved one another and were happy. Joseph, in his carpenter's shop, made lovely little wooden cradles, wooden yokes for the oxen, and ploughs for the farmers, saddles for the camels, chests and benches and stools for his own home with Mary.

But though they were happy, Mary and Joseph often talked gravely with their friends in the cool of the evening, when they sat out on the roof after the heat of the day. The presence of those Roman soldiers troubled them, as it troubled every Jew in their country. For it meant that their own land, the land which God had promised to Abraham so long ago, was their own no longer. The Roman Emperor had sent his armies and had conquered it, and now they were ruled from faraway Rome, and had to pay money to the emperor and to obey him. The Jews thought of the glorious days of King David, when they were a great nation, and wished with all their hearts to be a great nation again, free in their own land.

Meantime they waited, for God had promised them a Saviour, a great King who should one day reign over them and save them from their enemies. They thought of Him with hope and longing, and remembered the words of the prophet of old—"Unto us a Child is born, unto us a Son is given; and His name shall be called Wonderful, Counsellor, the Mighty God, the Everlasting Father, the Prince of Peace".

One never-to-be-forgotten day an Angel came to Mary, as she sat alone in her room, and told her that she, simple Mary of Nazareth, had been chosen by God to be the mother of the King Who was to come, the Holy Child, the little Son of God.

And later the Angel came to Joseph and told him Mary's secret, and that he should love Mary and take care of her, and of the Holy Child, little Jesus, when He should come.

So Mary married Joseph and went to live with him in the little house by the carpenter's shop. Mary was happy all day, making things comfortable for Joseph, and Joseph was happy and busy in his carpenter's shop. Perhaps he made a specially beautiful little cradle with blue rockers for the time when the little Son of God could be laid in it.

So the days went quietly by while they waited.

Mary and Joseph Go on a Journey

One day a Roman soldier came riding into Nazareth, demanding to see the head man of the town. The children and the people gathered round to stare at him, wondering why he had come. They knew he was a messenger from the Emperor Augustus, known, like all the Roman emperors, as Caesar. The soldier read out to them a proclamation. Every man in the land was to go to his own home town, there to register his name, for all men were to be taxed.

Now both Joseph and Mary belonged to the House of David, that great King David who had once been a shepherd boy on the hills of Bethlehem. So the new decree meant that Joseph must go to Bethlehem, Royal David's city, to register his name.

So Joseph tidied up his carpenter's shop; Mary packed food for the journey, and also the baby clothes she had been making, in case they were needed, and Joseph bought a little grey ass for Mary to ride.

No one travelled alone in those days if he or she could help it, because in the wild, lonely rocky gorges there were often robbers, and wild animals too. So Joseph and Mary set off on the three days' journey with other travellers. Joseph took every care of Mary, but by the time they were at last climbing the hill that led to Bethlehem, they were very tired. It was late, dark but for the light of the stars, and cold.

Their troubles were not yet over. So many strangers had gone to Bethlehem that every house was full. Mary and Joseph went to the inn, but the innkeeper had only the same story to tell.

" My poor wife can go no farther," said Joseph sadly. "Is there *nowhere* she can rest?"

The innkeeper looked at them by the light of his lantern, and was sorry that he had no room. He said kindly, "At the back of the inn there is a stable in the rocks where I keep my own cattle. I will sweep out a stall for you, and give you clean hay and straw, and there you may rest until the morning."

And in the quiet night-time, there, in that lowly cave, among the soft lowing oxen, Jesus, the little Son of God, was born.

How happy Mary was! She wrapped her Baby in the

long, soft linen bands she had prepared for Him; she called them swaddling clothes. Joseph filled a manger with clean, sweet hay, and they laid the Baby in it, surrounding Him with the hay to keep Him warm, and there He went sweetly to sleep.

Mary lay back to rest on the fresh straw, and Joseph covered her with his long cloak, and sat beside her to keep watch over her and the sleeping Baby. The oxen lowed softly and were still. All was peace and quiet in that humble little room among the rocks of Bethlehem.

It was the first Christmas Morning!

The Angel and the Shepherds

The little town of Bethlehem slept, but out in the hillside fields were shepherds minding their flocks beneath the quiet stars. They sat in the doorway of the sheepfold, with their dogs around them, talking quietly together but keeping watchful eyes open for intruders. For sometimes wolves prowled around, and sometimes thieves, so the good shepherds never left their sheep unguarded.

That night the shepherds were probably talking of the

new tax they had to pay, and of all the travellers they had seen climbing the hill to the town.

Some of the travellers were possibly staying in the shepherds' own homes that night. So they spoke of these things together, wishing for the coming of that great King Who was to make them once more a great nation.

"The prophet has said that He will be born in Bethlehem," said one of the shepherds. "I wonder when He will be born. And how shall we know when He is here?"

And suddenly, strangely, as if in answer, the dark hill

The shepherds knelt before the tiny babe

The visit of the Wise Men

field was lit by a great light. The shepherds looked up in wonder, then scrambled to their feet in amazement and fear. For shining down on them was God's bright messenger, an angel, and the glory of the Lord shone round about them. The shepherds fell humbly to their knees, wondering and afraid.

But the angel cried to them, "Fear not; for behold, I bring you good tidings of great joy, which shall be to all people. For unto you is born this day in the city of David a Saviour, which is Christ the Lord. And this shall be a sign unto you; ye shall find the Babe wrapped in swaddling clothes, lying in a manger."

And suddenly there was with the angel a multitude of angels, the whole sky was filled with them, all praising God and singing over and over again, "Glory to God in the highest, and on earth peace, good will toward men".

The shepherds looked up, but now their fear was turned to joy. While the heavenly music lasted they spoke no word, but looked and listened with all their might, repeating the beautiful words in their hearts, that they might not forget them. Gradually the music died away, the light faded, the angel returned again to heaven, until all was as it had been, a quiet starlit sky glimmering down on the quiet sheepfold upon the hillside. But it was not exactly as it had been. For in the hearts and minds of the shepherds had dawned a great excitement, joy, wonder and delight.

"He is come!" they cried to one another. "He is born to-day in Bethlehem. Let us hasten thither. We must find Him, that we may love and worship Him, the little Son of God, our promised Saviour."

They left their dogs to guard the sheep and hurried up the hill together. "We shall find Him lying in a manger, the angel said. But where?" asked one. "We will ask at the inn first."

But when they entered the town, all was quiet and still. The people slept; they knew nothing of the shepherds' wonderful news. The inn was dark too, but one of the shepherds saw the pale glimmer of Joseph's lantern in the little rock stable. "See! The stable has a light!" he whispered. "There will be a manger there. Come! Let us see!"

They crowded closely together and peeped in. Yes, there was the Baby, just as the angel had said, lying in the manger. Mary and Joseph were surprised when the men came softly in, asking for the little Son of God, and when they told all they had heard and seen that night, their wonder grew. The shepherds knelt before the tiny Baby, adoring and thanking God that at last their promised Saviour had been given to them. Then they went joyously away, to tell everyone the wonderful tidings given to them, the simple shepherds of Bethlehem.

And Mary, alone again with Joseph and her Baby, thought of all these things—of the angel's message to her, of his message to Joseph in a dream, and now of the shepherds' glad tidings. What had the angel said? "I bring you good tidings of great joy, which shall be to all people." "To all people!" Mary must share her Son with all the world and the angels in heaven, but for a little He would be hers alone to love and care for. And Mary kept all these things and pondered them in her heart.

The Visit of the Wise Men

Now there lived, far away in the East, certain Wise Men, who had made long and careful study of the stars. One night they saw a new star, so bright that none of them had ever seen such a one before. They thought it must herald the coming of a great King. They had heard and read of the King foretold by the prophets, One who should be King of the Jews, whose Kingdom should have no end.

This must be His star. The three Wise Men determined to go to seek Him, that they might worship Him.

They made preparations for a long journey, and took with them gifts for the King of the shining Star. One took ornaments of gold, one a casket of sweet-smelling incense, and the third a jewelled box of myrrh.

When all was ready, they set off, travelling by night, that they might be guided by the bright shining Star, leading them ever on towards the land of Palestine, and at last they came to the city of Jerusalem.

So it was that one day the Roman sentry by the city gate saw a great cavalcade coming along the way. In front rode three magnificently dressed men, on camels whose trappings were studded with gold and silver, and the riders looked like kings.

They halted before the sentry at the gate, and leaning from their saddles asked him, "Where is He that is born King of the Jews? For we have seen His Star in the East, and are come to worship Him."

The Roman soldier stood very straight as he answered proudly, "There is no king but Caesar. In Jerusalem Herod rules in Caesar's name. Go, and ask of him."

So the Wise Men rode into the city, and they asked the people in the street their strange question, "Where is He that is born King of the Jews?" so that all the people were talking of the magnificent strangers and their quest. Was not Herod king of the Jews? What, then, was this talk of a guiding Star and a king newly born? And they were troubled.

And in his palace King Herod himself heard the news —heard it with fear and furious anger. Herod was crafty and cruel, the Romans despised him, the Jews hated him; he knew this and was always afraid of losing his throne and his power. If he thought any man was a danger to him, he had that man put to death at once.

He sent for the Jewish high priests and rulers, and asked them concerning the prophecies of the King who was to come. He asked them where the Christ was to be born, and they told him, "In Bethlehem of Judaea."

Then Herod sent secretly for the Wise Men and talked to them alone. He told them to go to Bethlehem, and when they had found the Christ, to return to Jerusalem with the tidings, pretending that he himself wished to go and worship Him also. But in his wicked heart he meant to do nothing of the kind.

That night the Wise Men set off joyfully upon the short

journey to Bethlehem, and this time the Star moved across the sky before them, until it stood over the place where little Jesus was. Eagerly entering, they found Mary and Joseph and the little Child, and they bowed themselves down and worshipped Him, humbly offering Him the rich gifts they had brought.

Then they went away rejoicing and praising God. For the rest of that night they slept at the inn, and as they slept God warned them in a dream not to return to Jerusalem. So when they awoke, they returned to their own country another way.

And on the next night the angel of the Lord came again to Joseph and said, "Arise, and take the young Child and His mother, and flee into Egypt, and there stay until I bring word. For Herod will seek the young Child to destroy Him."

So Mary and Joseph prepared for their journey. Before they could start, they had to buy food for the journey, and they needed a donkey, too, so that Mary could ride and carry the infant Jesus in her arms. When they were ready, they stole secretly away in the night and began their long journey over the sandy desert.

They arrived in Egypt safely, and there they lived in peace for a time.

The little Lord Jesus was safe. But back in Bethlehem there were sorrowful hearts and many tears. For wicked King Herod, when he found that the Wise Men did not return, was furious with rage. He sent his soldiers to Bethlehem with orders to kill every baby boy of two years old or under. What a terrible thing to do! The people were sickened and horrified, and they hated King Herod more than ever.

But at last that evil king died, and then once more, to Joseph in faraway Egypt, the angel of God appeared in a dream, saying, "Arise, and take the young Child and His mother, and go into the land of Israel; for they are dead which sought the young Child's life."

How gladly Joseph and Mary prepared for that return journey to their own land! Now they could live among their own friends once more. And they decided that they would go back, not to Bethlehem or Jerusalem, but to their own little town of Nazareth. For in Jerusalem the son of Herod was king, and he was cruel and wicked like his father.

So it was in quiet little Nazareth that Jesus grew from babyhood to boyhood, where He grew in strength and wisdom, where He was happy in the love of God, father and mother, and all who knew Him.

"And the Child grew, and waxed strong in spirit, filled with wisdom; and the grace of God was upon Him."

Jesus of Nazareth

The Bible does not tell us much about the childhood of Jesus, but we know the countryside He lived in, and the kind of home He had with Mary and Joseph in the little white

house on the hillside, where the doves crooned in the sun-shine and green vines grew about the walls.

Jesus would watch His mother as she spun thread, or ground corn to make their daily bread. He would go with her to the well, and help to fill the waterpots which always stood beside the door, with several green leaves in the mouths of them to keep the water cool. He would watch His father as he sawed and planed in his carpenter's shop. On the Sabbath Day He would go with His parents to the synagogue and learn of God, His Heavenly Father, and hear the stories of Abraham and Moses, King David and Daniel.

When the time came He would go to school with the other boys, a strange school, where were no forms, no books, no blackboards; where the pupils sat on the floor before the teacher, and learned their lessons by heart—lessons of the Laws of God, very long and very difficult.

We know that Jesus must have known well, and loved most deeply, the countryside around His home, and the country folk who lived there. He knew the shepherds, the farmers, the fishermen. He saw how the shepherd guarded his sheep by day and night, calling each one by name, *leading* his flock to fresh pastures, and if one were lost, never resting until it was found and carried safely back to the fold. He knew how the farmers ploughed with their oxen yoked together, how they sowed their seed broadcast, so that some fell by the wayside, knew their joy when the harvest was good. He loved the flowers and the birds and the cool shade of the trees; the sunshine and the wide starry skies of night. We know all this, because when He became a Man, He told many wise and understanding stories of the simple things and people of His everyday life in Nazareth.

Every year, in springtime, Joseph and Mary went up to Jerusalem to attend the Feast of the Passover, a great festival for the Jews, commemorating the time when Moses led the Israelites out of Egypt. Jews from all over the world went up to attend the special services at the beautiful Temple, and to rejoice with their friends.

When Jesus was twelve years old, His parents took Him with them for the first time. It was a very happy occasion for Him. At last He would see the wonderful city of Jerusalem, and visit the glorious Temple, there to join in the services and to promise to obey God's Law.

The people travelled in a great company, and it was an exciting adventure for the children. Everyone enjoyed the journey in the sunny spring weather, the children interested in all the sights on the crowded roads. And what a

thrill it was when, at the end of the third day, they stood on Mount Olivet and saw the Holy City before them, its towers and pinnacles shining in the sun!

They stayed in the city for three days, and Jesus attended the services and listened to the wise Rabbis, the teachers of the Law. But none knew, except His father and mother, that the Boy listening with the eager, earnest face, was really the promised King Himself.

The time came to return to Nazareth, and the company gathered in chattering groups. Jesus was not with His parents, but they were not worried, thinking He must be with some of their friends behind. But when night came and they looked for Him, no one had seen Him. Then they *were* alarmed, for a boy alone in a strange city might be in great peril. Mary and Joseph hurried back to Jerusalem and sought Him in the crowded streets for three days, but all in vain. At last they thought of returning to the Temple, and there they found Him. To their great surprise Jesus was sitting with the learned men there, asking and answering questions, and making those wise men think very seriously, for they were amazed at the wisdom and knowledge of this Boy from the countryside.

"Son," said Mary, "why hast thou thus dealt with us? Thy father and I have sought Thee, sorrowing," and Jesus answered, "Wist ye not that I must be about my Father's business?" He meant that now He was growing older He must be preparing to do His work on earth for His Heavenly Father. But He went at once away with Mary and Joseph, back to Nazareth, and there He lived quietly and happily in obedience to them.

Jesus Chooses His Friends

Jesus lived in Nazareth until He was thirty years old, for His mother, Mary, needed Him. Joseph had died, so while His brothers and sisters were growing up, He stayed with His mother. But the time came when He felt that now He must begin His work for God, His Heavenly Father. So He said farewell to Mary, and went away—first to the River Jordan, where a wonderful new preacher, John the Baptist, had been teaching the people, and baptising them in the river as a sign that they wished their hearts washed free from sin.

When John saw Jesus walking towards him, he knew at once Who He was. "Behold!" he cried, "Behold, the Lamb of God!" And when Jesus wished to be baptised, John at first refused. "I have need to be baptised of Thee," he said. But Jesus still wished it, so John baptised Him, leading Him down into the river. As they came up again out of the water, a light shone from heaven, and John heard a Voice from heaven saying, "This is My beloved Son, in Whom I am well pleased."

Jesus knew that He would need help to do His work—men whom He could trust and teach, to carry His words far and wide, men who would believe in Him, and follow Him always.

One day, by the Sea of Galilee, He met two brothers, Andrew and Simon, who were fishermen. Andrew and Simon had two friends, who were also brothers and fishermen. The four young men often sailed their boats to-

31

gether, and they would share the fish they caught. One day they were all on the shore washing and mending their nets. They were not feeling very happy, for although they had sailed about all night they had come back to land without any fish.

"Today," they told one another, "we shall have nothing to sell."

As they were working Jesus came near, walking on the shore. How glad they were to see Him! It helped them to forget their wasted night. Jesus saw the empty boats and stepping into one of them—it belonged to Simon—he asked the men to row Him out just a little way from the land. In this way He could teach the people without being pressed by the crowd which soon gathered wherever He went. Now He sat down in the boat and talked, and all the people listened gladly.

Afterwards Jesus asked Simon to take his boat into deeper water and let down a net to catch the fish which Jesus knew would be found there. Simon did not expect to catch any fish in the daytime while the sun was shining brightly, but he said to Jesus, "Master, we have toiled all night and have taken nothing, but at your word I will let down the net."

This time everything was different. The net filled so quickly that it began to break with the weight. Simon and Andrew called to James and John for help. There were so many fish that both boats were filled and it seemed almost as though they would sink.

The fishermen were frightened and felt they were not good enough to be friends of Jesus, but Jesus spoke kindly to them and said, "Follow Me, and I will make you fishers of men." They looked up, and what they saw in His face made them instantly leave their boats and follow Him.

Jesus gave Simon a new name and so he was called Simon Peter. These four were Jesus's first friends and disciples, and He loved them dearly. Later He chose eight more men to join them, but those four fishermen seemed always closest to Him.

JESUS THE MERCIFUL

One Sabbath Day

It was in the country about the Sea of Galilee that Jesus began His work for God. Around the lovely lake in those days were many busy cities, where lived Romans, Greeks, and other races, besides the Jews. So that it was a countryside where very many people could hear Christ's message when He began to teach.

He taught in the churches—the synagogues—on the Sabbath Day, and the people crowded to hear Him. He taught on the beaches, and on the mountainsides, and men left their nets, and left the fields, and women and children came flocking from the houses, to listen to His message. He told them of the Kingdom of God, the Kingdom of Love. He talked to them of the way they loved their children, and worked for them. God, Jesus told them, was their Heavenly Father, and, "If ye then know how to give good gifts unto your children, how much more shall your Father Which is in Heaven give good things to them that ask Him?"

Jesus talked to them of all sorts of ordinary things—of birds and flowers, of seed-sowing and sheep-minding, of daily bread, and water from the well—speaking in simple, beautiful words that all could understand, and He healed the sick and the sorry, the deaf and the dumb and the blind.

Jesus spent much time in a city called Capernaum, where Peter and Andrew lived. One Sabbath Day, when He had been preaching in the synagogue there, He afterwards went home with Peter to his house. When they arrived, they found trouble, for Peter's wife's mother had fallen very ill. Peter asked Jesus if He would help, and Jesus spoke comfortingly to them all. Then He went to the sick woman and took her by the hand. At once she felt quite well, and got up and helped to serve the meal that was being prepared.

The news of her recovery soon spread among the crowds around the house—people always followed Jesus wherever He went. Some of them went away, but only to spread the news further, and to fetch neighbours or friends of their own who were ill. And that evening, in the glowing sunset light, they brought many sick and lame and weary ones to Jesus, and Jesus healed them every one.

All this work was very tiring, so that, when at last Jesus and His disciples were free to go to rest, they were wearied out. But Jesus got up very early before it was day, and slipped away to a quiet hillside, there to pray and gain new strength from God, His Heavenly Father.

When Peter and the rest got up later, they at once

missed Jesus, and set out to find Him, for already there were people asking for Him at the house. Peter guessed that his Master might have sought some peaceful place, and at last they found Him. Jesus greeted them with a smile; they said to Him, "All men seek for Thee," and the people following begged Him to stay with them. But Jesus explained that He must preach the Kingdom of God, and do His work, in other cities also.

So He and His disciples went to all the cities in Galilee, and Jesus taught the people and healed the sick, and great multitudes followed Him from the country around, and from Jerusalem and Judaea, and from beyond the river Jordan, for His fame went throughout all the land.

The Soldier's Servant

In every city and town in Israel Roman soldiers were stationed to carry out the orders of the emperor. In Capernaum there was an officer who had under him one hundred soldiers. He was called a centurion. This Roman officer liked the Jews among whom he lived, and he did all that he could for them. He built for them a beautiful synagogue in the city, of which they were very proud.

Now it happened that a servant of this friendly Roman soldier fell ill with palsy. The poor man shivered and shook, and could not keep still, so ill he was like to die. His master was very fond of him, and was deeply distressed at his illness, for no one seemed able to cure him. The centurion knew of Jesus, and of the wonderful power of healing that Jesus possessed. Would He, he wondered, come and heal the servant who was so dear to him? He hesitated to ask Jesus himself, for Jesus was a Jew, and he was a Roman, and he thought humbly that Jesus might not think him worthy of help. So, for his servant's sake, he went to the chief men of the synagogue he had built, and he asked them to go to Jesus for him. They went very gladly, and when they had found Jesus, they told Him all about the sick servant and his master, and how the centurion had befriended their people, and they gave Jesus the soldier's message—"Lord, my servant lieth at home sick of the palsy, grievously tormented."

Jesus said at once, "I will come and heal him."

But meanwhile the sick man's master had been thinking. He felt sorry he had troubled the Master to come to his home. He had such faith in Jesus that he believed there was no need for Him to see or touch the man. After all, he thought, if I want anything done, I have only to say to my soldiers or my servant "Do it" and it is done. Jesus is able also to command, and if He only says the word, my servant will be healed.

So he sent other friends to meet Jesus and to say to Him: "Lord, trouble not Thyself, for I am not worthy that Thou shouldst come under my roof; wherefore neither thought I myself worthy to come unto Thee; but speak the word only, and my servant shall be healed. For I also am a man set under authority, having soldiers under me; and I say unto one 'Go!' and he goeth, and to another 'Come!' and he cometh; and to my servant 'Do this,' and he doeth it."

Jesus listened to this message, and His face lighted up with surprise and pleasure. This man, this Roman, had greater faith in Him than had many of His own people. The greatest happiness Jesus had was to find trust and belief in Him in a man's heart.

He turned to His disciples and said: "I have not found so great faith, no, not in Israel."

When the messengers returned to tell the centurion what Jesus had said, they found everyone marvelling and joyful, for the beloved servant was quite well again, and his master's heart was filled with grateful praise. How happy the sick man must have been also! No doubt he went afterwards to see and hear and thank Jesus for himself, and to become with his master one of Christ's true followers.

The Widow's Son

In the city of Nain, in Galilee, lived a certain little family of father, mother, and small son. They were all very happy together, until one sad day when the father died. No one was left to look after the widow but her young son. He tried to comfort his mother—she must not be afraid, he would work for her, he promised, and take care of her. And he kept his promise, working for her and helping her in every way. His mother loved him with all her heart and was proud of him.

But one day the kind and loving son became ill and in spite of his mother's tender care, he died. Now indeed the poor woman was left desolate! Her neighbours came to help her, but she cried and grieved heartbrokenly. Everyone was very sorry for her, for they had loved the young man too.

The day came when the funeral must take place. The boy's body was placed on a bier, which was carried by four of his friends. His mother walked in front, sobbing bitterly, and the neighbours cried aloud and mourned too. A long procession followed, for everyone wished to show that they shared the poor mother's sorrow.

They came to the gate of the city, and passed through, but they had gone only a little way farther when they met a crowd of people about to enter, and in the midst walked Jesus.

When Jesus saw the poor mother, He stopped and spoke to her tenderly. "Weep not!" He said.

Then He went to the bier and touched it, and the four friends who bore it stood still, looking at Jesus in hope and wonder. What was this Man with the kind and gracious face about to do?

Jesus said: "Young man, I say unto thee, arise!"

And the young man sat up, and looking about him, he smiled at his mother and began to speak, and Jesus drew her gently towards him. Her arms went round her boy, and they laughed and cried together, hardly able to believe the truth, and all the multitude of people rejoiced with her, praising and glorifying God. They crowded round the widow and her son, they crowded round Jesus and His disciples. "A great prophet is here with us!" they cried, "and God hath visited His people." The story of the miracle spread far and wide, and all men wondered at the power and the authority of Jesus.

Storm-Tossed

Jesus had been teaching and healing all day, and by eventide He was wearied out. He walked down the beach and got into Peter's little ship, and He said, "Let us pass over unto the other side."

So the disciples sent away the crowds of people, and prepared to sail across the lake. Jesus, spent and weary, went to lie down in the stern of the ship, His head on an old pillow, and almost before Peter and James and John had the sails set, He was fast asleep. The disciples let Him sleep, for He needed the rest. The little ship glided smoothly along, the men talking quietly lest they disturb His slumber. Behind them, other little ships were following, for when people saw that Jesus was crossing, they determined to cross too, some hoping to see more miracles, others eager to hear His words.

It was getting dark. Peter looked anxious, and so did James and John, for the sea was rising, and away in the gorges of the hills they could hear the wind howling. If only they could get across before the storm broke, they would be safe. But the storms of wind in the Sea of Galilee are very sudden, and all at once the tempest swooped upon them. With an awful, deafening roar the wind came, buffeting and beating them. The waves rose

mountains high, crashing over the little ship and filling it with water. The fury and the noise were terrible!

But in the midst of the tumult, Jesus lay peacefully sleeping.

The storm got worse. Tossed like a cockleshell, the little ship laboured gallantly, but the frightened disciples knew that she must soon be swamped. They would all be drowned, with the men in the other little ships following.

They could bear it no longer. "Master!" they cried to Jesus, waking Him at last, "Master, carest Thou not that we perish?"

Jesus, opening His eyes, saw at once their danger. He stood up, and raising His hand, He spoke to the wind and the water—"Peace, be still."

And immediately a great calm came to the troubled seas. The wind died down, the towering waves became light ripples lapping on the ship, once more riding smoothly along. The wind and the waves had obeyed the voice of their Lord.

Jesus turned to His disciples. "Why are ye so fearful?" He asked. "How is it that ye have no faith?" for He wished that they had trusted Him more, that they had been sure no harm could come to them while He was there.

As they baled out the water, the disciples were filled

with awe and wonder. "What manner of man is this," they said to one another, "that even the wind and the sea obey Him?"

The Man with Four Friends

One day Jesus was visiting Capernaum, and when people heard that Jesus had come, they flocked to the house where he was staying to hear Him speak about God. It was a fine house, with a little staircase at the side, which led up to the flat roof of the house.

Jesus told the people crowded into the house and overflowing into the courtyard how God wished them to behave, and while they were listening, four men drew near. They were carrying a paralysed man who could not walk. The man was lying on a mattress, and the friends held the four corners. They carried the man very carefully, although it must have been a difficult job for them. They felt sure that if their sick friend could be brought to Jesus he would be cured.

The four friends managed to make a way through the crowd as far as the doorway, but here the people were so closely packed together that they could go no farther. They decided that they would take the sick man up the little stairway on to the roof, where they found that the

47

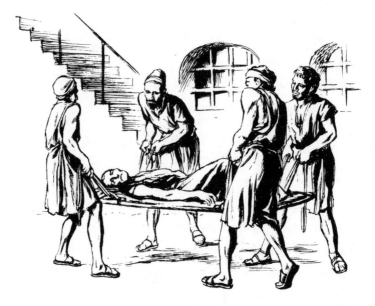

owner of the house had laid strips of wood across from one part of the roof to the other to keep the heat of the blazing sun from the courtyard. Across the wood strips were laid leafy branches. It was just a matter of minutes before the men had made a big hole in the roof.

Down below in the courtyard the people heard noises above them and looked up to see what has happening. To their amazement, down came a bed, lowered by ropes held by four pairs of strong arms—down, down, down to the ground at the feet of Jesus. The people *had* to make room for him now.

Jesus stopped speaking, and He looked at the man on the bed with kind eyes. Then He said something which must have surprised the people standing near. "Arise, and take up thy bed, and walk." And as his friends looked on, they saw the man get up, roll up his mattress, and tuck it under his arm. Then, smiling his thanks to Jesus, he walked through the crowded courtyard to the door.

Quickly his friends rearranged the branches over the courtyard and hurried down the stairs to meet him. Home they went, full of thanks to Jesus.

Little Talitha

Jesus had been across the lake to a wild, lonely place, where he had cured a poor wandering madman, and sent him home to his friends whole and well. Then He and His disciples sailed back again, and as they landed, a great multitude greeted Him gladly.

Amongst the crowd was a man in great trouble. His name was Jairus, and he was a ruler of the synagogue. He knew Jesus, and believed in Him with all his heart.

Now Jairus had a little daughter, whom he loved very dearly. We do not know her name, but we might call her Talitha, which was what Jesus called her when He spoke to her. It is a word that means "damsel". No doubt the little Talitha had seen and heard Jesus speaking in the synagogue, and knew His voice, and the kind smile He had for children. But now the little girl was very ill, and her anxious father had come to seek Jesus and ask His help. Flinging himself at Jesus's feet, he cried: "My little daughter lieth at the point of death; I pray Thee, come and lay Thy hands on her, that she may be healed; and she shall live."

Jesus turned at once to go with him. So many people pressed around, following Him, it was impossible to hurry. Presently Jesus stood still, then, turning about, He said, "Who touched my clothes?" His disciples gazed at Him in astonishment. A multitude of people were thronging Him, and in the surging crowd many must have touched Him. But Jesus knew that it was not just the pressure of the crowd. He knew that someone had touched Him purposely, touched Him with the touch of true faith, and that that someone had been healed. So He looked about Him, and waited.

Out from the crowd, fearing and trembling, stepped a poor woman, who fell at His feet, and told Him that she was the one who had touched Him. For years she had been ill, had spent all her money trying to get well; but no doctor had done her any good, and she had got steadily worse. She heard of Jesus, the great Healer, Who freely and lovingly used His great power to do good, and so she sought and followed Him, for she said to herself, "If I may touch but His clothes, I shall be whole." Slowly she had drawn nearer and nearer in the crowd, until she was near enough to stretch out her hand and touch His garment, and at once she had felt herself whole and well again. Jesus listened while she told Him all this. Then he smiled at her tenderly, calming her fear, saying, "Daughter, thy faith hath made thee whole; go in peace."

All this time poor Jairus had been fretting in his heart at the delay, and at that moment he saw some of his own servants pressing near to speak to him. Frightened and dismayed, for he knew they brought bad news, he waited. "Thy daughter is dead," they mourned as they reached him, "why troubleth thou the Master any further?" Poor Jairus was too grief-stricken to speak.

But Jesus had heard, and turning, spoke comfortingly to him. "Be not afraid, only believe." For those who had trust in Him, Jesus could do all things. So they went on together.

When they reached the house, they found a terrible commotion—crowds of neighbours and friends weeping and wailing because the little girl was dead. Jesus spoke to them quietly: "Why make ye this ado and weep? The damsel is not dead, but sleepeth." But no one believed Him. They could not understand that the spirit of the child was not dead, and that Jesus knew He had the power to call it back again to this world.

Jesus commanded that all should go outside, save only her father and mother, and His disciples. Then He went into the room where the little girl lay, so pale and still. For a moment He stood looking down at her. Then bending over her, He took the small, cold hand in His warm one, and said: "Talitha, cumi"—"Damsel, I say unto thee, arise."

And at His words, the spirit of the little girl came back. The closed eyes opened, and she looked into the kind, loving face of the Lord Jesus. Then she sat up, and still holding Jesus's hand, walked to her joyful father and mother.

Jesus told them to give her something to eat, and then, telling them not to talk about what He had done, He slipped quietly away, leaving behind Him hearts full of joy and praise.

The Boy with the Loaves and Fishes

Jesus had sent out His twelve disciples to preach the gospel of the Kingdom of Heaven. They had been given power to heal the sick, the blind, the deaf and the dumb, and to raise the dead in the name of Jesus. Now they had come back to Him, and He was longing to hear how they had fared. But Jesus was kept so busy teaching and heal-ing that He and His disciples had scarcely time to eat. So they sailed quietly away across the Sea of Galilee to find some far place among the hills where they might rest a while in solitude.

When the people saw Jesus departing, great crowds set off on foot, hurrying by the shore road and across the green plain to find Him among the wild hills.

There was to be no rest for Jesus, but His loving heart could not be angry with the people, for He felt sorry for them. So patiently He sat down and began to teach them many things, and to heal their sick. All day they lingered with Him, until the sun was setting. Then the disciples begged Jesus to send the multitude away, that they might go into the villages to buy bread, for they had nothing to eat, and soon darkness would be upon them.

Jesus said to them: "Give ye them to eat."

His disciples were greatly astonished—how could they feed such a multitude in that deserted place? Philip, an-swering, said: "Two hundred pennyworth of bread is not sufficient for them, that every one of them may take a lit-tle."

Now among the crowd there was a boy with a basket upon his head. In the basket there were five barley loaves and two small fishes. He was most likely a baker's boy, who, selling his loaves among the crowd, had followed them when they followed Jesus. He may have intended to eat these five small loaves remaining, for his own dinner. But all day long he had listened to Jesus, and watched Him at work, so absorbed and interested that he had forgotten all about eating. Now, with a glad heart, he remembered and knew there was something he could do for the Master he was learning to love so dearly. He offered his basket to Andrew, and Andrew took him to Jesus. "There is a lad here," he said, "which hath five barley loaves and two small fishes. But," he added doubtfully, "what are they among so many?"

Jesus, with a smile of thanks for the boy, took the basket and bade the disciples make the people sit down in companies upon the grass. When this was done, and all the hungry people were sitting wondering and expectant among the grass and the wild flowers, Jesus took the basket, and after giving thanks to God and blessing the bread, began to break up the loaves and fishes, and gave them to the disciples, who took them to the people, going and coming again and again until all that great gathering, about five thousand, had eaten and were satisfied. How the boy's eyes must have glistened with awe and wonder and delight, as he stood there and watched his five loaves and two fishes feeding such a multitude! Never would he forget it!

When all were satisfied, Jesus said: "Gather up the fragments that remain, that nothing be lost," and when this was done, there were twelve baskets full of the pieces that were left.

Then a splendid hope shone in the eyes of the excited people and stirred their hearts. "This is of a truth that Prophet that should come into the world," they said to one another, meaning that they believed Jesus to be their promised Saviour. They would make Him a King, He should lead them against the Romans, and they would win glorious victories, and become free and great.

But Jesus, watching their excited faces, knew their thoughts. They had misunderstood when He talked of the Kingdom of God. For He had come, not to be rich and great, but to be the Friend of the poor and unfortunate, and to teach all men of their Father in Heaven.

So Jesus sent the multitude away, and told His tired disciples to sail away home, and He Himself went higher up the mountain, to pray alone in the peace of the darkening hillside.

The Lord of the Sabbath

Every day Jesus was performing miracles of healing, and teaching in the Temple and the synagogues; and many of the people loved and believed in Him with all their hearts. "He hath done all things well," they said as they talked over some of the miracles they had seen Him do. "He maketh both the deaf to hear and the dumb to speak," and they believed Him to be the Christ, their Saviour Who should come.

But there were others, the Pharisees and the rulers of the Temple in Jerusalem, who hated Jesus. (The Pharisees were Jews who prided themselves on the strictness with which they kept the laws of their religion, but often they made too much of details and forgot that God asks for goodness of heart first of all.) They were jealous of His power, and sought to prove that He was deceiving the people. He broke the Sabbath laws, they said, because He healed folk on the Sabbath Day. He was wicked, for He said sometimes when He healed the sick, "Thy sins be forgiven thee." Only God could forgive sins, said the enemies of Jesus, and they watched and spied upon Him to find an excuse to take Him prisoner.

One Sabbath Day He was teaching in the synagogue, and the scribes and Pharisees were there watching and listening. Among the people in the congregation there was a poor man who had a withered arm: his right arm was shrunken and useless. Would Jesus heal him on this Sabbath? The Pharisees were watching, ready to accuse Him if He did so. But Jesus was never afraid of them. He knew exactly what they were thinking, and He said to the crippled man, "Rise up, and stand forth in the midst," and the man stood up before all the people, his eyes shining with hope.

Then Jesus turned to the scribes and Pharisees, and said: "What man shall there be among you that shall have one sheep, and if it fall into a pit on the Sabbath Day, will he not lay hold on it, and lift it out? How much is a man better than a sheep? Is it lawful to do good on the Sabbath Days, or to do evil? to save life, or to kill?" and Jesus looked at them sternly, waiting their answer. But there was dead silence; they could not answer Him.

Jesus said to the man with the withered arm, who had been listening anxiously, "Stretch forth thine hand," and at once the useless arm came up, whole and strong again.

Then, while the happy man gave thanks to Jesus, the enemies of the Lord went away, mad with anger, to plot with other men how they might kill Him.

But Jesus went quietly away with His disciples, and went on with His work for God, and in spite of the malice and hatred of the Pharisees, multitudes followed Him and believed in Him.

THE GREAT TEACHER

Teacher and Friend

People often asked questions of Jesus as He talked to them, sometimes very difficult questions, just to see if He could answer, and of course Jesus always could give them a wise and right reply. One day a certain clever man stood up and asked what he must do to gain the life everlasting.

Now Jesus was aware that the man knew the answer perfectly well, so instead of answering directly, He asked a question in His turn. "What is written in the Law?" He said. "How readest thou?" The lawyer answered instantly: "Thou shalt love the Lord thy God with all thy heart, and with all thy soul, and with all thy strength and with all thy mind; and thy neighbour as thyself."

"Thou hast answered right," said Jesus. "This do and thou shalt live."

But the lawyer asked another question: "Who is my neighbour?" he said.

Then Jesus told a story to show that our "neighbour" means anyone to whom we can be kind or helpful; and that we should treat him in the way we should like to be treated ourselves.

One day, along the lonely mountainous road from Jerusalem to Jericho, there came a traveller. This was a dangerous road to walk alone, for robbers lurked among the dark caverns in the rocky gorge, and so the traveller hurried on, anxious to reach his journey's end before nightfall. But even as he went, the unseen robbers leapt on him. They beat him cruelly, stripped him of his clothes, and took away all he had, leaving him wounded and helpless by the roadside.

For long the poor man lay there bleeding and half dead. Oh, if only someone would come along to help him! At last he heard footsteps approaching. Hopefully his eyes flew open. A priest was coming near, a priest from the Temple of God—surely he would help! But when the priest saw the poor torn and bleeding man, he hastily crossed over to the other side. He knew quite well what had happened to the unfortunate traveller, and he did not want it to happen to himself. He hurried away.

Presently came the sound of other footsteps. This time it was a Levite travelling the road. He came and looked down at the helpless man, who thought that a Levite, a man who served in the Temple, might perhaps be kind to him. But the Levite also crossed over and hurried away.

The poor man shut his eyes once more. For long he lay there, and when towards evening he heard the sound of a little ass trotting along the road, he did not trouble to open his eyes. This traveller would pass also, he thought, but close to him the pattering footsteps stopped. Someone came and looked down at him. Then he did open his eyes, and saw that the stranger was a Samaritan, from whom he could expect no help, for Jews and Samaritans were enemies.

To his surprise the stranger did not pass on. Instead, he knelt down and gently tended the wounds with oil and wine, and bound them up carefully. Then he helped the poor man on to his own little ass, put his own cloak around him, and led him along the way until they came to an inn. Here the Samaritan got the landlord to help put the wounded man to bed, gave him drink and food, and took every care of him.

The next morning, before he left, the Good Samaritan gave money to the innkeeper, and said: "Take care of him, and whatsoever thou spendest more, when I come again, I will repay thee."

When Jesus had finished telling the story he said to the lawyer who had questioned Him: "Which now of these three, thinkest thou, was neighbour unto him that fell among the thieves?"

The lawyer answered: "He that showed mercy on him."

Jesus said: "Go, and do thou likewise."

The good Samaritan

His father's loving eyes recognized him

The Lost Sheep

Among the people who came to listen to Jesus there were often men who had not lived good lives—men who had sinned against God and their fellow men. Some of the very strict Jews said that Jesus should not talk to these people, or eat in their houses, as He often did. So Jesus told them stories to show that God loved all men, and wanted them in His Kingdom of Love.

He remembered how, many years before, as a boy He had often watched the shepherds on the hillsides caring for the sheep and lambs. He told a story about one particular shepherd who had one hundred sheep. This kind man was kept very busy looking after his large flock. During the day he led them to places where they could find fresh grass to eat and water to drink. The sheep wandered about, but the shepherd watched them, and when they strayed too far he would go after them and bring them back. At night he brought them together in one place, and there he would light a fire to frighten away any wild animal who

65

would harm the sheep. Later, he would lie down, wrapped in his cloak, and sleep until morning.

One evening he collected his sheep before sunset and began to count them as he always did, one, two, three, and so on. Then the good shepherd discovered he had only ninety-nine sheep, and he was sad when he found that one sheep was missing, so he went off to search, although by this time it was beginning to be dark.

Up and down the hillsides he went, listening, and calling to the poor, silly sheep that had roam away from the safe place. Thorns scratched his face and hands, and his sandals were cut by rough stones, but still he went on.

Then, when the shepherd was very tired, he heard the bleating of the lost sheep, and soon his search was over. He forgot his long walk, and picking up the sheep he laid it on his shoulders and took it back. He was very happy that he had found the missing sheep and rejoiced that he was taking it safely home.

"Which of you," said Jesus, "having an hundred sheep, if he lose one of them, doth not leave the ninety and nine in the wilderness, and go after that which is lost, until he find it? And when he hath found it, he layeth it on his shoulders, rejoicing. And when he cometh home, he calleth together his friends and neighbours, saying unto them: 'Rejoice with me, for I have found my sheep which was lost.'"

So, Jesus told them, there is great joy in heaven when one sinner repents. And Jesus Himself had come to seek and to save the sinners, the lost sheep of His Heavenly Father, and to bring them again into God's Kingdom of Love.

Then Jesus told a story to show how gladly God will give his love and pardon to any sinner who humbly and sincerely asks His forgiveness.

The Boy who went Astray

There was once a certain rich man who had two sons. These boys had a happy home, with good things to eat, fine clothes to wear, servants to wait on them, and best of all, a father who loved them dearly and cared for them in every way.

When they grew up, the younger son became tired of living on the quiet farm. He wanted to go out to see the world, to find pleasure in the big cities, with money to spend. He became discontented, and while his elder brother worked steadily, and obeyed his father in all things, this younger boy just idled his time away. At last he went to his father and asked if he might have at once that share of his father's money which would some day be his. Though grieved that the young man was tired of his home, the father divided his money and gave to his

younger son his share, which was enough to make him feel rich and independent. Delighted, he said a careless farewell to his father and brother, and set off on his travels to the city. There he spent his days in pleasure, in feasting, folly and wickedness, until all his money had gone.

And when he had spent everything, there came a great famine in the land, and he was hungry and in trouble. Those who had been friends when he was rich did not help him at all, now that he was poor. At last he was obliged to go and beg humbly for work, that he might eat, and a certain man sent him into the fields to mind his pigs. Still no

69

one gave him anything to eat, and he was so hungry that he shared the food given to the pigs.

While he sat there, hungry and miserable, his thoughts went back longingly to that comfortable home he had left so carelessly, to his kind and loving father, and he began to see how selfish and wrong he had been. He thought of all his father's servants; they had plenty to eat, food and to spare, while he was perishing with hunger.

At last, ashamed and wretched, he made up his mind to

return and ask his father's forgiveness. "I will arise," he thought, "and go to my father, and will say unto him: 'Father, I have sinned against heaven, and before thee; and am no more worthy to be called thy son; make me as one of thy hired servants.'" To be a servant in his father's house would be happiness enough for him now.

He wasted no time, but set off at once on that long, weary journey home, trusting in his father's love to forgive him and allow him to stay there.

So it was that one day his father saw, coming along the road, a sad and weary figure, clad in rags and limping on sore and tired feet. The old man had never ceased to think of his young son, to wonder what had happened to him, to grieve that he heard no word from him. Now, as he watched, something in that forlorn figure seemed suddenly familiar. He looked, and looked again—could it be? It was—his own son returning! His father's loving eyes recognized him through all the dust and the grimy rags, and not waiting until he should reach the house, out along the road the old man ran to meet him. The young man saw him coming, and, with tears running down his face, as he stood there, ashamed and sorry, felt his father's arms around him, and a loving kiss upon his cheek.

"Father," he began, as soon as he could speak, "I have

sinned against heaven, and in thy sight, and am no more worthy to be called thy son—"

Before he could say any more his father called to his servants: "Bring forth the best robe, and put it on him, and put a ring on his hand, and shoes on his feet. And bring hither the fatted calf, and kill it, and let us eat and be merry; for this my son was dead, and is alive again; he was lost and is found."

How happy, how humble, how grateful the wanderer must have felt when he found himself once more in his father's house, well clothed, well fed, well beloved, with everyone rejoicing around him!

The Story of Zacchaeus

One day Jesus and His disciples were passing through Jericho, and as usual the people were pressing around Him. Crowds lined the way to see Him pass, to hear His voice and to get near Him, and among the throng was a little man named Zacchaeus.

Now Zacchaeus was a tax collector, and all the tax gatherers were hated by the people. So often they were dishonest, demanding more money than they should, and keeping it themselves, so that they became very rich. Zacchaeus was a rich man, for he had robbed the people in this way too. Sometimes he felt ashamed of himself, for he knew that he had cheated and done wrong. Though he was not altogether wicked, the people of Jericho would have nothing to do with him. He was a sinner, they said, and they despised and hated him.

Now Zacchaeus had heard of Jesus, of His teaching, and the wonderful things He did, and he was determined to see Him for himself. But the crowd was dense, and as Zacchaeus was a little man, he could not see over the heads of the people. No one would give way to him, to let him through to the front. They just pushed him back—he was only Zacchaeus, the hated tax collector.

The little man could tell by the shouts of welcome that Jesus was drawing nearer. What could he do? How get to see Him? Suddenly he had an idea. He turned and ran to a sycamore tree which overhung the way, and climbing into it, crawled out along a branch which spread across the path. He could see finely now. Peeping through the leaves, he could see Jesus coming in the midst of the throng. He knew Him at once, by the beauty and goodness in His face. Nearer and nearer He came, while Zacchaeus, hidden among the branches, watched Him with eager eyes. When Jesus stood directly beneath him, Zacchaeus had a great surprise. For the Master lifted His head, and looking straight at him, said: "Zacchaeus, make haste and come down, for today I must abide at thy house."

Zacchaeus nearly fell out of the tree in his excitement. How did Jesus know that he was there—and how did he know his name? The little man was filled with joy, Jesus

was coming to his house! He rushed home and prepared a feast for the Master and His disciples, and when Jesus came, all was ready, and Zacchaeus welcomed Him joyfully.

As Jesus with His disciples sat at the meal, the people

crowding outside murmured that He had gone to be the guest of a man who was a sinner.

Zacchaeus heard, and was sorry and ashamed that Jesus should hear it too. But Jesus, of course, knew all about it, and He still looked kindly at the little tax collector and talked to him wisely and well. And as Zacchaeus listened, he knew that he could never cheat again. He jumped up and stood before Jesus, and said in a loud voice, that all might hear: "Behold, Lord, the half of my goods I give to the poor; and if I have taken anything from any man by false accusation, I restore him fourfold."

And as they heard, and looked into the happy face of their Master, the disciples knew that He had been right to stay in the house of a sinner. For because He had done so, He had round the goodness hidden in the heart of Zacchaeus, who now would lie and cheat no more, but would love God and serve Him.

The Grateful Heart

It was springtime in Palestine. The rains were over, the sun shone in a blue sky, and the flowers began to bloom in the fields and on the mountainsides. Jesus and His disciples were on their way to Jerusalem, to attend once more that Feast of the Passover to which Jesus had first been taken when He was twelve years old.

On the way they passed through Samaria and Galilee, and as they drew near a certain village one day Jesus heard husky voices calling to Him—calling anxiously for help: "Jesus, Master, have mercy on us!" Afar off, standing in a little group among the rocks, were ten men who were suffering from the terrible disease of leprosy. They dared not come near; all they could do was to call and ring their bells to warn others to keep their distance. Jesus looked pitifully at them, and spoke kindly to them, but all He said was: "Go, show yourselves unto the priests."

At once they turned to go, but as they went their dim eyes grew bright, their withered flesh firm and clean, their weak and husky voices clear and strong. They were well again!

They shouted and sang and leapt for joy along the way as they went to seek the priests to pronounce them cured. But presently one of them turned back and went hurrying to Jesus. He fell at Jesus's feet, and with tears of love and gratitude he thanked Him, and glorified God. Now that man was a Samaritan.

And Jesus said: "Were there not ten cleansed? But where *are* the nine? There are not found that returned to give glory to God, save this stranger." Jesus called him a stranger because he was a Samaritan and not a Jew. Then Jesus said to the kneeling man: "Arise, go thy way, thy faith hath made thee whole."

Jesus and the Children

Jesus loved the children, and they loved Him, and loved to listen to the stories He told. But sometimes there were so many grown-ups eagerly crowding round Jesus that the children could not come near.

One day when Jesus was busy teaching many people, some mothers drew near with their little ones. They hoped that Jesus would lay His kind hands on the children, and bless them. Eagerly they sought to get through the crowd, but the disciples, seeing them, tried to prevent them, saying that Jesus was too busy to be bothered by the children just then. The mothers were turning disappointedly away, but Jesus had heard, and He called to the disciples: "Suffer

the little children to come unto Me, and forbid them not, for of such is the Kingdom of heaven."

Joyfully the women turned, as Jesus held out his arms

to the children, and lifting them one by one, He blessed and loved them. Then He gave them back, with kind and gentle words to their happy mothers.

The Blind Beggarman

It was blossoming springtime in the green country around Jericho. Outside the gates of the city a blind man sat begging by the wayside. The sun shone warm on his face; a little breeze refreshed him. As he sat there, he could not see the passers-by, but he could hear their footsteps. There were many footsteps that day, for the pilgrims were going up to Jerusalem for the great feast of the Passover. As Bartimaeus, the blind man, listened, he knew of excitement among the people, of a great crowd going by, and he called out eagerly to know what was happening. Someone stayed to tell him that it was Jesus of Nazareth passing by.

Immediately Bartimaeus began to cry out with a loud voice: "Jesus, thou Son of David, have mercy on me!" Many tried to silence him, but he only cried louder still: "Jesus, thou Son of David, have mercy on me!"

Jesus stopped, and asked those around to bring the

blind man to Him. So they ran to Bartimaeus, and said encouragingly: Be comforted, rise, he calleth thee."

Then Bartimaeus, leaping to his feet and casting off his cloak in his eagerness, hurried to Jesus.

"What wilt thou that I should do unto thee?" asked the Master, and Bartimaeus begged: "Lord, that I might receive my sight."

Jesus answered him: "Go thy way, thy faith hath made thee whole." And at once the blind man's sight came again. He could see! He looked into the kind and understanding eyes of Jesus; he knew the lovely blossoming world, the excited faces of the crowd. The joy in his heart overflowed as he praised God for His mercy, and he turned and followed Jesus in the way.

In Bethany

Six days before the Feast Day, Jesus and His disciples came to Bethany, the little town near Jerusalem where His friends, Mary and Martha, and their brother Lazarus, lived; where Jesus loved to stay, and where He had worked His greatest miracle. Once when He had come to Bethany he found that Lazarus, His friend, had died, and had been buried for four days. Yet, when Jesus called him, Lazarus had come forth from the tomb alive and well. Many people believed in Jesus when they saw this, but others had gone away to tell the chief priests and the pharisees what Jesus had done. The rulers of the Temple, angry and alarmed, began to plot and to plan to put Jesus to death.

Now Jesus, on His way to Jerusalem, tarried again in quiet little Bethany with His friends, and one, Simon, made a supper, a feast, for Him. Martha was serving, and Lazarus was one of those who sat at table with Him. Then came Mary, with precious ointment, and anointed the feet of Jesus, so that the whole house was filled with the perfume of it.

Then many of the Jews, hearing that Jesus was at Bethany, came, not only to see Him, but to see Lazarus also, whom He had raised from the dead. And when the chief priests saw how, because of him, so many people were forsaking *them* and believing on Jesus, they planned to kill Lazarus also. So the danger for Jesus and His friends grew.

The Name of Jesus of Nazareth was on everyone's lips. There was great excitement among the people. Would Jesus come to the Feast? Would He come as their Leader to banish the Romans and become their king? Would he dare to proclaim Himself openly as the Son of God, in the Temple, where His enemies had taken up stones to stone Him?

But Jesus was afraid of nothing man could do to Him, for He knew that He had done perfectly the will of His father in Heaven. He knew too, exactly what was to happen to Him in Jerusalem. He had warned His disciples on the way: "Behold," He said, "we go up to Jerusalem, and the Son of Man shall be delivered unto the chief priests and unto the scribes; and they shall condemn Him to death. And they shall mock Him, and shall scourge Him, and shall kill Him; and the third day He shall rise again."

But the disciples had not understood. They loved and believed in Him, and could not imagine such evil coming to their beloved Master. But one of them, named Judas, listened in dismay. He had hoped and expected that Jesus would be a great and glorious king on earth, and that *he* would share in the glory. But Jesus was talking of betrayal, capture, and death that sounded like failure. Judas Iscariot was disappointed; he wanted riches and power. Was he not to have them?

Jesus Rides into Jerusalem

The day after the supper at Bethany, Jesus and His disciples came to the Mount of Olives. Jesus rode upon the foal of an ass which His disciples had fetched for Him. When the people saw that He was really going to Jerusalem, there was tremendous excitement. Now, they exulted, the Master was going to proclaim Himself their king, to free them from the Romans and all their enemies.

With a great shout of joy they surrounded Him, and a glad procession followed Him. Many flung their garments in the way, others cut down branches from the trees, and strewed them in His path, and all the company of His disciples, men, women and children, began to praise God for all the mighty works that they had seen, crying, "Hosanna to the Son of David! Blessed is He that cometh in the name of the Lord; Hosanna in the highest!" Then came many from the tents on the hillside to meet Him—numbers were Galileans from His own countryside—bearing palm branches; and, having met Him, they turned and went before Him, chanting: "Hosanna to the Son of David! Blessed is He that cometh in the name of the Lord. Hosanna in the highest!"

Hearing the cheering, crowds came pouring through the gates of Jerusalem, asking eagerly: "Who is This?" to be answered joyfully: "This is Jesus, the prophet of Nazareth of Galilee."

So Jesus rode, heralded like a king, among the excited and joyous people. Yet when, looking across the valley, He saw the lovely city shining on its opposite hillside, and the roofs of the Temple gleaming in the sun, and the people streaming through the gates, Jesus stopped. And suddenly He was shedding tears of deep sorrow. He knew that

Jerusalem was going to reject Him, and, through Him, His Father who sent Him; but His tears were not for himself, but for the woes that should come, when the Temple should be burnt down, the city destroyed, the people left desolate.

The multitude watched in wonder. "Why did the Master weep, among the cheers and rejoicings?" Presently He went on again, down through the valley, and up to the gates of the city, and so through the narrow streets, and the surging, cheering throngs, straight to the Temple. And here He began to teach and to heal, doing good as He had always done.

When the chief priests and the scribes saw the wonderful things that He did, and heard the children crying, "Hosanna to the Son of David!" they were angry, and told Jesus to make the children stop singing such words, for this meant that the Master was the king. But Jesus looked tenderly at the children, and smiled as He listened, refusing to stop them. "Have ye never read," He said to the priests, "Out of the mouths of babes comes the most perfect praise?"

And when it was eventide, Jesus left the thronging city, and went back to the quiet of little Bethany among the palm trees, and the loving companionship of His friends.

THE SAVIOUR OF THE WORLD

Jesus in Jerusalem

Jesus had entered Jerusalem like a king, with cheering crowds surrounding Him. And for those few days before the great Feast of the Passover, He taught in the Temple, and healed the sick as He was wont, while the children in the Temple courts sang joyfully, "Hosanna to the Son of David!" and the people listened to Him eagerly. There were many strangers in the jostling streets, besides the Jewish pilgrims who had come from far lands to the great festival in the holy city. They came crowding to hear the wonderful prophet Who taught that all the people of this earth, and not only the Jews, were the children of one loving God, and so were brothers and sisters to one another. And Jesus now openly declared that He was the Son of

God, sent from His heavenly Father to become, not the king of any nation upon earth, but to be the King of love in men's hearts, that He might draw them all into God's own kingdom.

But in the palace of the High Priest the enemies of Jesus, the priests and the Pharisees, who thought his teaching wrong and dangerous, plotted to take Him prisoner. They dared not do this openly, for they feared the people might rush to rescue Him, and as Jesus was always surrounded, they did not know how they could do it.

Then, two days before the Feast Day, came to them secretly Judas Iscariot—that disciple of Jesus who loved power and riches, and who was disappointed that Jesus re-

fused to become a great king on earth. Now, seeing how angry the priests and the rulers were, he was afraid of getting into trouble himself. So he went to the palace secretly, and offered, if they would pay him money, to betray Jesus to the priests in some lonely place where no one could rescue Him.

The priests were only too glad to pay for this wickedness, and they gave Judas thirty pieces of silver. The priests were to bring soldiers, and after dark he would take them to a quiet garden where Jesus often used to go in the evenings, and there they could take Him prisoner without interference from the people.

The Last Meal Together

Jesus and His disciples were in an upper room in Jerusalem, where supper had been made ready for them. Even Judas was there, with his terrible secret in his heart. But it was no secret to Jesus. Jesus knew that He was to be betrayed by Judas, and put to death by the priests. He sent Judas away, and then he talked to the others, trying to prepare them for the sorrowful time they would go through.

He knew that when He was not with them their hearts would be exceedingly sad, and they would be greatly troubled. So he spoke most lovingly to them, telling them beforehand all that should happen, and promising them that when He had gone, they should receive a comforter from God. At the time they did not understand all that He said, but in the days to come they were to remember and rejoice.

Jesus said to them, "Yet a little while I am with you. Ye shall seek Me, but whither I go, ye cannot come. A new commandment I give unto you, that ye love one another; as I have loved you, that ye also love one another."

Peter, most eager of disciples, asked, "Lord, whither goest Thou? Why cannot I follow Thee now? I am ready to go with thee, both into prison, and to death."

Brave words, and Peter meant them, but Jesus, knowing his strength and his weakness, answered sadly, "I tell

thee, Peter, the cock shall not crow again for another day, before thou shalt thrice deny that thou knowest Me."

For long Jesus talked to them, speaking words of warning, of comfort and cheer, and at last He blessed them, saying, "Peace I leave with you, My peace I give unto you. Let not your heart be troubled, neither let it be afraid."

Presently they sang a hymn, and then went out.

In the Garden

So they came to the Mount of Olives, to the quiet, moonlit little garden of olive trees, called Gethsemane, a place which Jesus often visited. Most of the disciples stayed near the gate, but Jesus, taking Peter and James and John, went away among the trees. He was feeling very sad and lonely, knowing that the people He had loved and taught would turn against Him.

Asking the three to watch with Him, Jesus went a little apart from them to pray to His Heavenly Father for strength and courage to face the terrible pain and suffering which He knew was coming. Though Jesus was the Son of

God, He was a Man too, able to feel pain and loneliness as all men feel at times. And in this dark hour of sorrow, of grief for the sin and suffering in God's beautiful world, He almost felt it would be more than He could bear, yet He prayed, "Not My will, but Thine, be done." He knew that this was why He had been sent into the world, that He should suffer and die to save the people from their sins, and though He had saved others from pain, Himself He would not save.

When we feel sad or lonely, when we have pain to bear, hunger or thirst or weariness, we can remember that Jesus bore it all before us, that He knows how we suffer, and will help us when we pray, as His Heavenly Father helped Him. After Jesus had prayed to God for the third time, and went back to the three—who had fallen wearily asleep— His face was strong and peaceful. Now He had strength to bear His heavy burden.

"Rise," He said to Peter and James and John. "Rise, let us be going. Behold, he is at hand that doth betray Me."

Even as He spoke, there came the sound of tramping feet, as with lanterns and torches, and the clatter of arms, a band of soldiers, with the chief priests, marched into the garden. In front walked Judas, the traitor. Straight to Jesus he went, and greeting Him, "Master! Master!" he kissed Him.

Jesus said to him, "Betrayest thou the Son of Man with a kiss?"

The disciples, aghast, had scrambled to their feet, and as the soldiers laid hands on Jesus, Peter angrily drew his sword and cut off an ear of one of the servants of the High Priest. But Jesus would not have fighting. "Put up thy sword," He said to Peter. "Thinkest thou that I cannot now pray to my Father, and He shall send Me more than twelve legions of angels?" Then He leaned over and touched the ear of the wounded man, and at once it was whole again.

Then Jesus spoke to the priests, "Are ye come out, as against a thief, with swords and staves to take Me? When I was daily with you in the Temple ye stretched forth no hands against Me, but this is your hour and the power of darkness."

Then the soldiers bound Jesus and surrounded Him. The disciples fled away.

Jesus was left alone with his enemies.

Through the narrow streets, lit only by their swinging lanterns, the rough soldiers hustled Him away, straight to the palace of the High Priest, and when they had passed through, the great gates were shut fast behind them.

In the Palace

Now Peter and John, sorrow and dismay in their hearts, and anxious to know what happened to their beloved Master, had followed afar off.

John was known to the keeper of the gates, so when he asked permission, he was allowed in, and he took Peter with him. They went into the great court. Jesus stood at the far end, bound and helpless, being questioned by the

priests, and when He answered, He was struck, mocked and reviled.

Peter stayed with the servants, near a fire which had been made, for the night was cold. As he sat there warming himself, one of the maids came by. Staring hard at Peter she suddenly said, "This man was also with Him," and she asked Peter, "Art not thou also one of this man's disciples?"

But Peter, startled and afraid, denied it. "Woman, I know Him not."

Shortly afterwards another saw him and said, "This fellow was also with Jesus of Nazareth." Again Peter denied Him, "I do not know the man."

Time dragged by, while Jesus, given no rest, was kept standing, continuously answering questions, mocked and despised by the priests.

Then came one who, looking at Peter, said confidently, "Of a truth this fellow also was with Him, for he is a Galilean." And another said, "Did I not see thee in the Garden with Him?"

Once more Peter's courage failed. He denied it with oaths and cursing. And while he was yet speaking he heard the cock crow!

Jesus turned and looked at Peter, and Peter remembered

how Jesus had said, "Before the cock crow thou shalt deny Me thrice."

And as his eyes met the sorrowful eyes of his beloved Master, Peter's heart was like to break with grief and remorse. He rushed away into the darkness, and wept bitterly.

Jesus before Pilate

All that night Jesus was hurried from one judge to another. Before the council of the scribes and elders, the High Priest asked Him, "Art Thou the Christ, the Son of God? Tell us." But when Jesus answered "I AM," "He is guilty of death!" they cried, and they mocked Him, and struck Him with their hands.

The Jews themselves could not condemn anyone to death, so early in the morning of the next day— which was Friday, the day before their Sabbath— they took Jesus to Pontius Pilate, the Roman governor.

Pilate governed Jerusalem for the emperor of Rome. It was his work to keep peace and order in the city. If there should be trouble, riots and disorder, Pilate himself would

Jesus rides into Jerusalem

Jesus before Pilate

be in disgrace. So when, outside his Castle of Antonia, a multitude appeared, making a great clamour, and bringing in a prisoner, it was his duty to judge the dispute.

Inside the judgment hall Jesus stood before the governor, while the Jews accused Him of many things. Pilate could not understand their rage against this quiet, noble-looking man. None of the things of which He was accused seemed to the governor worthy of death. The prisoner had called Himself Christ, a king, he was told. Pilate was puzzled. He asked Jesus, "Art Thou the King of the Jews?"

Jesus answered, "My kingdom is not of this world. If My kingdom were of this world, then would My servants fight, that I should not be delivered to the Jews."

Pilate said, "Art Thou a king then?" and Jesus answered, "Thou sayest that I am a king. To this end was I born, and for this cause came I into the world, that I should bear witness unto the truth."

Pilate went out to the waiting Jews. "I find no fault in this man," he declared.

It was the custom, in honour of the Feast of the Passover, that the governor should free from prison some notable prisoner. Pilate wished to release Jesus. So now he asked the crowd, "Will ye that I release unto you the King of the Jews?" But this made the Jews angrier than ever.

"Not this man," they shouted. "Not this man, but Barabbas!"

Now Barabbas was a robber, imprisoned for dreadful crimes.

Pilate spoke again. "What will ye then that I shall do unto Him whom ye call the King of the Jews?" and the answer came fiercely, "Crucify Him! Crucify Him!"

Again Pilate tried to save Jesus. "Why, what evil hath He done?" he demanded. "I will scourge Him and let Him go." But again came the cry, more furious still, "Crucify Him! Crucify Him!"

Pilate, to satisfy their rage, ordered that Jesus should be cruelly beaten. The soldiers led Jesus away. They plaited a crown of thorns, and put it on His head. They dressed Him in a purple robe of state, and bowing the knee, they mocked Him, despising Him, "Hail! King of the Jews!"

Once more Pilate led Jesus forth, still wearing the crown of thorns, and in terrible pain from the beating. The governor hoped that the people's hate might now be satisfied. "I find no fault in Him," he said again.

But the cry was still the same, "Crucify Him! Crucify Him! We have a law," the Jews cried to Pilate, " and by our law He ought to die, because he has made of Himself the Son of God."

The *Son of God*!

Pilate, greatly afraid, led Jesus aside again, and asked Him who He really was. But Jesus would not answer until Pilate said, "Knowest Thou not that I have power to crucify Thee, and power to release Thee?"

Jesus replied, "Thou couldst have no power at all against Me, unless it were given thee from above."

Pilate was awed and mystified. Again he tried hard to save this innocent Man, but the Jews only cried more furiously, "Away with Him! Crucify Him!"

"Shall I crucify your King?" asked Pilate.

"We have no king but Caesar!" came the shout. "If thou let this Man go, thou art not Caesar's friend."

Then at last, seeing that no words were of any avail, but that trouble and tumult were brewing, Pilate commanded that Jesus be crucified.

So, surrounded by rough soldiers, still wearing the crown of thorns, and bowed beneath the heavy cross, Jesus was led away to a terrible death.

And one man, who saw him go, was filled with horror and remorse. It was Judas, the traitor. When he saw that Jesus was really going to be put to death, he repented of his dreadful crime. He rushed away to the priests. He flung their money before them. "I have sinned!" he cried.

But they only mocked at him, and unable to bear his own thoughts, he rushed away again and hanged himself in despair.

On a Hill called Calvary

On a hill called Calvary, Jesus, with tearing nails through His hands and feet, hung for hours on the cruel cross, while great crowds came to watch Him in His pain, many to mock, but many to mourn. At the foot of the cross stood some of the women who loved Him best, and among them His own mother, Mary. Poor Mary! She remembered in her sorrowing heart the little stable in Bethlehem where her baby was born, the angels' song, the shepherds, the Wise Men and the shining star; the flight into Egypt, and the quiet years when Jesus was a boy in Nazareth, and the three years when he had gone about teaching of God, and doing good—nothing but good—and now, how sad and bewildering it must have been to her to see her beloved son hanging there on a cross between two thieves! Was this to be the end of it all?

Jesus, looking down on His weeping mother, even in

His own pain thought of her, and calling to John, the disciple whom He loved best, and who was standing near by, He told him to take Mary into his own home and be as a son to her; John, only too glad to obey this last request of his beloved Master, led Mary away.

Then a great and terrifying darkness came over all the land. The earth quaked, rocks were rent, and through the darkness the soldiers near the cross heard Jesus cry, "It is finished. Father, into Thy hands I commend My spirit."

Jesus was dead, and a great fear fell on all those about the cross and those who had come to watch. As the darkness rolled away, many returned to Jerusalem in terrified misery, sure that a great wrong had been done.

The captain of the Roman soldiers, who had watched all through the long hours of Jesus's suffering, seen His kindness for His mother, and heard His words of promise to one of the thieves hanging beside Him, now declared, "Certainly this was a righteous Man; truly this was the Son of God!"

There was a rich man named Joseph, of Arimathea, who loved Jesus. He went boldly to Pilate and begged that he might take away the body of his Lord. Pilate gave him leave, and so Joseph and his friend Nicodemus took down the body of Jesus from the cross, wrapped it in fine linen with spices, and laid it in a new tomb belonging to Joseph—a tomb cut in the rocks of a garden nearby. When all was in order they rolled a great stone to the entrance and went sorrowfully away. Some of the women who loved Him had followed to see where He was laid. Then they, too, went away to spend the Sabbath Day quietly.

Then to that still garden came the Jews, having worried Pilate for permission. They set a great seal on the stone before the tomb, and a guard of soldiers to watch it. They had remembered that Jesus had said He would rise again from the dead, and they were afraid His disciples might steal His body and then declare that He had so risen.

The First Easter Day

The Sabbath Day passed quietly, but very early on the Sunday morning, before it was light, Mary Magdalene and some of the other women came to the garden with spices and perfumes they had prepared for anointing. As they came, they said to one another, "Who shall roll us away the stone from the door of the sepulchre?" for the stone was very heavy. But when they reached the garden they saw that the stone was already rolled away, and the soldiers had vanished. Amazed, they stooped and went into the sepulchre.

The body of Jesus was gone, but sitting there they saw a shining angel. They were frightened, but the angel said to them, "Fear not, for I know that ye seek Jesus of Nazareth, which was crucified. He is not here, for He is risen, as He said; behold the place where the Lord lay. But go your way quickly, and tell His disciples and Peter, that He is risen from the dead; and behold, He goeth before you into Galilee; there shall ye see Him, as He said unto you."

The women, trembling, but with joy in their hearts, ran to do the angel's bidding, and Mary Magdalene ran to tell Peter and John. "They have taken away the Lord out of the sepulchre," she cried breathlessly, "and we know not where they have laid Him." Peter and John rose hastily and ran back with her, and coming to the garden they saw the empty tomb and the clothes which had wrapped Jesus lying folded nearby. Still they did not understand that Jesus was really alive, and troubled and wondering, they returned to Jerusalem.

But Mary Magdalene stayed beside the tomb, weeping bitterly. Once she stooped and looked again into the tomb.

There were two angels sitting, one at the head, the other at the feet, where the body of Jesus had lain. The angels said to her, "Woman, why weepest thou?"

Mary answered, "Because they have taken away my Lord, and I know not where they have laid Him." As she spoke, she turned back, and there was Jesus standing behind her. But Mary, with her eyes full of tears, did not know Him. Jesus said to her, "Why weepest thou? Whom seekest thou?" and Mary, thinking Him to be the gardener, answered, "Sir, if thou have borne Him hence, tell me where thou hast laid Him, and I will take Him away."

Jesus said one word, "Mary!"

And Mary, hearing her name spoken in that beloved voice, knew Him at last. "Master!" she cried joyfully.

To the disciples, where they mourned and wept, Mary sped with her glad tidings. "I have seen the Lord," she cried eagerly, and told them all that Jesus had said. Still they could not believe that He was really alive; but that night, as they sat together in a locked room, in secret for fear of the Jews, Jesus Himself came and stood among them, and said, "Peace be unto you!"

Then, as He saw they were afraid, He showed them the nail wounds in His hands and feet, and the great gash in His side where a soldier had thrust his spear. And as they looked and listened and clustered about Him, touching Him, hearing His beloved voice comforting them, their mourning was turned to gladness. This was their own dear Master. They had watched Him in pain upon the cross, they had mourned Him as dead, they had seen the place where He was buried. But death could not hold Him; the Lord had risen, as He had told them He would. Jesus Christ was alive for evermore, and an overpowering joy filled the hearts of his disciples.

Now on that night, Thomas, one of the disciples, had not been with them, and when they told him, "We have seen the Lord," he could not believe. "Except I shall see in His hands the print of the nails, and put my finger into the print of the nails, and thrust my hand into His side, I will not believe."

A week later the disciples, and Thomas with them, were again met together; and suddenly Jesus was with them, saying, "Peace be unto you." Then, looking at Thomas, Jesus said, "Reach hither thy finger, and behold My hands; and reach hither thy hand, and thrust it into My side; and be not faithless, but believing."

But Thomas, the moment he saw the Lord, had believed. No need to touch Him. "My Lord and my God!" cried Thomas joyfully.

Jesus said: "Thomas, because thou hast seen Me, thou hast believed. Blessed are they that have not seen and yet have believed."

After this, though Jesus did not again live and walk with His disciples every day, they saw Him many times during the following weeks. In these meetings their Master explained to them all that they were to be His messengers on earth, carrying His teaching to all people. "As My Father hath sent Me, even so I send you," He said. "Go ye into all the world and preach the gospel to every creature. And lo, I am with you always, even unto the end of the world."

There came a day when Jesus led them out as far as the little town of Bethany, where He had so often stayed. And there Jesus explained to them that now the time had come for Him to return to His Heavenly Father, and they would see Him no more on this earth. But they should not be left uncomforted, for God would send them His Holy Spirit, to live in their hearts and help them to live nobly, keeping the commandments that Jesus had given them, carrying His message to all men, bringing others into the kingdom of God's love.

Even as they watched Him with eager, adoring eyes, and Jesus smiled one last lovely, loving smile at them, He was lifted up from the earth, and a cloud received Him out of their sight.

For a long time they stood gazing up into the heavens. Then, talking joyfully together, they went back over the Mount of Olives to the city of Jerusalem, there to await the coming of the Holy Spirit, to prepare for their great task, and to obey always their Lord's commandment:

"My little children, love one another."

UNTO ALL NATIONS

A New Beginning

It was harvest time in Canaan, and the great Feast of Pentecost, the Jews' harvest thanksgiving, was taking place. In Jerusalem the streets were crowded with people—Jews from all parts of the land, and from many faraway cities and countries—and all were bearing offerings of corn, wine and fruit, which they were taking in thanksgiving to the Temple. It was a joyful time.

But the followers of Jesus were gathered together in one place. It was the fiftieth day after Christ had risen from the dead, and His disciples were waiting in Jerusalem, as He had bidden them, for the fulfilment of His promise to send them the Holy Spirit to live in their hearts and comfort them.

Suddenly there came a sound out of heaven as of a rushing mighty wind. It filled all the house where the disciples were gathered together, and in the midst of that great sound there appeared to them flames, which rested upon each of them. They became filled with a great joy and power, and knew that the Holy Spirit of God had been given to them.

As that mighty sound swept over Jerusalem, crowds, pale with fear, poured into the streets, asking what it could mean. Soon the news spread that the great wind had shaken the house where the friends of Jesus of Nazareth were, and that fire from heaven had fallen on them.

Outside the house the crowds of people pushed and pressed, and as they drew nearer they were filled with amazement. Among them were men from all parts of the world—from Egypt, Rome, Mesopotamia, Arabia—men who spoke widely different languages. Yet as they stood there they heard the disciples, simple shepherds and fishermen who had never left their own land, speaking in the tongues of their far-away homes.

How could this be? Astonished, they asked one another, "Are not all these which speak Galileans? Yet now we hear them speak in our tongues the wonderful works of God."

But some of the Jews mocked, and shouted that the disciples must be drunk.

Then Peter, standing up before them all, began to speak to the jostling crowd. Peter, who only a few weeks before had been so afraid and cowardly that he had thrice denied his Master, was now filled with the strength and courage of the Holy Spirit, and boldly, fearlessly, he stood forth where all could see him, and spoke in a ringing voice.

He told them that Jesus of Nazareth, Who had done such wonderful things among them and Whom they had crucified, had risen from the dead. Now He had sent to them His Holy Spirit from Heaven, where He reigns for ever as Lord and Christ.

As Peter finished speaking the people stared at one another, in remorse. Had they really crucified their promised King, the Son of God Himself?

"Men and brethren, what shall we do?" they cried to Peter and the apostles.

Then Peter explained that Jesus had come to save all who repented, that the promise of forgiveness and the Holy Spirit was for every one of them. For long he talked to them, preaching Jesus and His message of love, and that day over three thousand people joined the disciples as followers of Christ.

Many of these, when they returned to their own homes, carried with them the story of Jesus and the teaching of the apostles. So the Gospel, the good news, spread and became known in faraway lands.

At the Gate Beautiful

One afternoon at the hour of prayer, came Peter and John to the Temple service. They walked together through the fine covered gallery called Solomon's Porch, and climbed the wide steps which led up to the great gate which was named Beautiful. Beautiful it was indeed, shining and beautiful, like pure gold in the sunlight. As they reached the top of the steps, a poor lame man lying there spoke to them, asking a gift. This unfortunate man was over forty years old, and never had he been able to walk. Every day friends carried him up to sit beside the Beautiful Gate, that he might ask alms of those who went to pray.

When the lame man spoke to Peter and John, they stood still, and Peter answered him, "Look on us." The lame man looked at them eagerly, hoping to receive a gift of money. But the gift they had for him was far, far better than any money. Peter, meeting his eager gaze, said to him, "Silver and gold have I none, but such as I have give

Jesus appears to Mary Magdalene

Stephen prayed, "Lord Jesus receive my spirit."

I thee: In the Name of Jesus Christ of Nazareth, rise up and walk." And he took the lame man by the hand, and lifted him up, and at once his feet and ankle bones became strong. Leaping up, he stood and walked and entered with them into the Temple, joyous of heart and praising God.

As the people round about saw the wonderful sight, they were filled with amazement. They all knew that this was the lame man who sat every day beside the Beautiful Gate, and the news of the miracle spread swiftly through the crowds. When Peter and John returned from the service, the lame man holding on to them as though he could not let them go, the people thronged around them in Solomon's Porch, staring at Peter and John, and greatly wondering.

"Ye men of Israel," said Peter to them quietly, "why marvel ye at this? or why look ye so earnestly on us, as though by our own power or holiness we had made this man to walk?"

And then he explained to them that it was faith in the Name of Jesus Christ which had made the lame man whole; Jesus, the Son of God, Whom they had rejected and crucified, but Whom God had raised up from the dead.

The people listened thoughtfully, and again many of them believed. Peter and John stayed with them until the evening, answering their questions and teaching them the Gospel. But as darkness fell came soldiers, sent by the angry priests and rulers of the Temple, and the two apostles were hustled off to prison.

The next day they were questioned by the priests, and threatened with dire punishment if they spoke again in the

Name of Jesus Christ of Nazareth. But Peter and John boldly and bravely answered that they must listen to God rather than to the priests, and must speak of the things which they had seen and heard. Since they had done nothing for which they could be justly punished, the priests had perforce to set them free, and day after day they went out teaching the people, and healing the sick in the Name of Jesus Christ of Nazareth.

Stephen, the Faithful

The apostles of Jesus had again been imprisoned by the Council of Priests and Pharisees, and so angry were these men that they would have put the apostles to death. But there was a wise man among them, a Pharisee himself, a leader and a rabbi honoured by the people, and this man, whose name was Gamaliel, warned the others to be very careful what they were about. "If this work," he said, meaning the teaching of the apostles—"If this work be of man, it will come to nothing; but if it be of God, ye cannot overthrow it, and beware lest it be against God that ye fight."

This made the others pause to consider his words. Then having beaten the apostles with rods, and forbidding them once more to teach in the name of Jesus, they sent them away.

The apostles went home, rejoicing that they had borne shame and suffering for their Master's sake, and day by day in the Temple, and in every house, they taught the Gospel of Christ Jesus, and for some time they were not molested.

But trouble was to come.

There was in Jerusalem a noble young man named Stephen. Stephen was full of faith and the Holy Spirit, and did many wonderful works among the people. He was a very clever speaker, able to argue and explain very clearly, so that when the rulers of the synagogues tried to prove to him that his teaching of Jesus was a great mistake and very wicked, Stephen answered them so wisely that they found nothing to say.

But this only made them more angry, and they plotted together to find some way of putting Stephen to death. They looked for, and found, men willing to tell lies about Stephen for money. Then they brought Stephen before the great Council of Priests, and there the wicked men cried aloud that they had heard him say wrong and terrible things against God and against Moses.

The Councillors listened, and they looked at Stephen with horror and anger. One young man especially—his name was Saul—felt his heart full of hatred against Stephen, for he really thought him very wicked, and worthy of death.

But Stephen looked calmly at them all, showing neither anger nor fear. Had not Jesus Himself warned His disciples that the time would come when they would be brought before judges, flogged, tortured, or put to death for His sake?

And as Stephen thought of his beloved Master, Who had suffered death for all men, his heart became filled with peace and love, so that everyone looking at him saw his face beautiful and serene as the face of an angel.

"Are these things so?" asked the High Priest, giving the young man leave to answer his accusers.

Then Stephen spoke for a long time, going back into history to the days of Abraham and Moses, David and Solomon, showing how time after time in the past the people had resisted God, persecuting the prophets, and killing many of God's servants. And last of all, Stephen accused his accusers; they themselves had betrayed and murdered the Saviour, the Son of God Himself.

During his long speech his hearers had been growing

more and more furious. But Stephen was not afraid. He was looking up with steadfast eyes into heaven, and there he saw the glory of God. His voice rang out once more: "Behold, I see the heavens opened and the Son of Man standing at the right hand of God."

At these words the storm burst upon him. Shouting with rage, his hearers stopped their ears, and rushing upon Stephen, bore him out of the Council chamber, hustled him through the crowded streets, out of the city gate, and along the rough road to a stony valley.

Stephen knew what they were about to do. He was to be stoned to death. Bound and helpless, but still serene, he watched them. The wicked men who had given false witness against him took off their coats and laid them at the feet of the young man named Saul. Then, stooping, they picked up great stones and hurled them at Stephen.

As the first stones crashed down upon him, Stephen prayed, "Lord Jesus, receive my spirit."

Then he kneeled down, and in the midst of his pain, as the terrible stones came thicker and faster, he remembered how Jesus on the cruel cross had prayed for his enemies: "Father, forgive them, for they know not what they do." So Stephen prayed for his enemies, "Lord, lay not this sin to their charge." And with these words, he fell asleep.

Stephen was dead, the first disciple to die for his Master's sake. His sorrowing friends carried him away and buried him with tears. They would miss him so much, and they knew well that this was only the beginning of sorrow and persecution for them. And so indeed it proved. For the followers of Jesus in Jerusalem were hunted down furiously, fiercely, and thrown into prison by their enemies. Many of them fled and were scattered abroad. And the fiercest of these enemies of Christ at that time was the young man Saul, who in his hatred entered into every house and dragged off men and women to prison.

But the disciples of Jesus who were scattered abroad went from place to place, preaching the Gospel of Christ to all men, and so still the good news spread, and more and more men and women joined the followers of Jesus.

Philip and the Stranger

After the death of Stephen, the disciples were scattered abroad, and Philip went to Samaria. There he preached the message of Jesus to the Samaritans, and worked many miracles of healing among them. The people listened with

great joy, and many of them believed and were baptised in
the Name of Jesus. Then Peter and John, hearing that
Samaria had received the word of God, went there to
them also, laid their hands upon them, and prayed that
they might receive the Holy Spirit from God. And to
these believers also, who were not Jews, God sent his
great Gift.

One day Philip, bidden by God, went down towards Gaza, through the desert. Towards him, riding in a handsome chariot, and with his guards and servants surrounding him, came a man from Ethiopia. In his own country this man had great power, for he was lord of all the Queen Candace's treasure. He had been to Jerusalem to worship at the Temple and was returning to his own land. As he rode, he read aloud from the Scriptures words of the prophet Esaias, and Philip, running alongside the chariot, heard him and asked if he understood what he was reading. The great man said that he could not, unless he had someone to guide him, and he prayed Philip to join him and explain to him as they rode along.

So Philip climbed up beside him, and told him all the good tidings of Jesus Christ, and the meaning of the Scriptures. His companion listened eagerly, and as they fared along the way they came to a stream of water. "See!" cried the Ethiopian, "here is water. Why may I not now be baptised?"

Philip answered, "If thou believest with all thine heart, thou mayest." "I believe that Jesus Christ is the Son of God," came the reply.

So the chariot was stopped, and Philip baptised the Ethiopian in the name of Jesus. Then, greatly rejoicing, the newly made Christian climbed once more into his chariot and went on his homeward way.

Philip had vanished, to preach God's Word in many towns and villages on his northward road, and there can be no doubt that the stranger from Ethiopia carried the story of Jesus to his own far-off land. So the good tidings spread abroad in the world.

Peter and Eneas

In a little town called Lydda, not far from Jerusalem, lived a man named Eneas. He was a most unhappy man. For eight years he had been ill upon his bed, shaking with that dread disease—the palsy. He could not keep his head or his body or his limbs still for one minute.

Eneas had friends who were disciples of Jesus, and perhaps he had heard how one day four friends of a poor man, suffering, like himself, from palsy, had carried the invalid to the house where Jesus was teaching. And when, because of the crowd, they could not get near the Lord, they had climbed to the top of the house, removed some of the roofing, and lowered the sick man down to the very feet of

Jesus. Jesus had said kindly, "Take up thy bed and walk," and immediately the man had risen up well and strong.

Eneas thought wistfully of this story. If only he could go to Jesus! But Jesus had been crucified. Eneas could not hope to be taken to Him now.

One day Peter came to Lydda. Peter was spending his time now going from place to place, encouraging and comforting the followers of Jesus, healing the sick, and teaching the people. It was a wonderful thing that the power of Jesus to heal the sick and the suffering had now, through the Holy Spirit, been given to the disciples also. Peter, on his arrival, was told of the sick man, and went at once to see him.

Full of the power of the Holy Spirit, Peter spoke in the Name of Jesus: "Eneas, Jesus Christ maketh thee whole; arise and make thy bed."

The twitching limbs became still. Eneas rose from his bed, strong and healthy, perfectly healed, and joy dawned in his heart, and gratitude to God.

Through the little town the news of the miracle spread quickly, and the people came crowding to hear Peter, and to see Eneas. Listening to Peter they knew he spoke truth, and many gave their hearts to the Lord Jesus.

The Lady of Kindness

In the little seaside town of Joppa lived a number of the disciples of Jesus. Among them was a lady named Tabitha —sometimes she was called Dorcas.

This lady was very rich, and might have spent her money in luxury and selfishness. But Tabitha had a heart full of love, and spent her money and her time in helping those not so fortunate as herself. She was especially kind to poor widows—women whose husbands had died and left them in poverty. She made garments for them and their little ones, befriended them in every way she could, and was very much beloved.

Now it happened that this kind lady fell ill and died, to the great grief of all her friends. Tenderly the women laid her body in an upper room, and made everything ready for her burial.

But meanwhile the disciples had been talking together. They knew that Peter was in Lydda, only nine miles away. They would send for him—Peter, their leader, who was healing so many in the name of Jesus. He might be able to help them. Two of them hurried off at once, and told Peter of their trouble.

Peter at once returned with them, and was taken to that upper room where Tabitha was lying so still and quiet. But the room was not quiet; it was full of the widows and Tabitha's other friends, weeping and wailing. They crowded around Peter, showing the garments Tabitha had made for them, telling of all her goodness, of how much they would miss her.

Peter spoke quietly to them, and sent them all away, as Jesus had once sent away the mourners from the room of little Talitha. Left alone with Tabitha, Peter knelt down and prayed to God. Then, knowing that, through the gift of the Holy Spirit, he had power to call back the spirit of Tabitha from the dead, he turned to her and said softly, "Tabitha, arise!"

The closed eyes opened, and when she saw Peter, Tabitha sat up. Peter, smiling at her, gave her his hand and helped her to rise. Tabitha stood there well and strong again, and Peter, calling her friends, showed her to them.

What a joyful day that was! All through Joppa the news spread, and again people crowded to hear Peter — townsfolk, sailors from the harbour, strangers and travellers landing from the ships—all heard Peter preaching the Gospel of Christ, and many more turned to the Lord Jesus.

The Rescue of Peter

For some time the apostles and followers of Jesus had been allowed to live in peace and to teach the Gospel unmolested, but now a new king, the grandson of that King Herod who had cruelly murdered the young children in Bethlehem so long ago, came to reign in Jerusalem. This king, named Herod Agrippa, was anxious to make friends with the Jews, and he knew that the rulers of the Temple hated the followers of Christ. So he sent soldiers to capture James, the brother of John, and had him put to death.

This was a terrible grief to the disciples, for they loved James very dearly. To add to their trouble, they feared that now the persecutions would begin again. It was only too true. Herod, when he saw how much the death of James pleased the Jewish rulers, made up his mind to please them still more.

It was springtime once again, the time of the great Feast of the Passover, and Jerusalem was crowded. Herod sent soldiers to arrest Peter, meaning, after the Feast was over, to put him also to death. Peter was cast into prison, and closely guarded, night and day, by soldiers in bands of four.

The disciples were overcome with sorrow at this news. How could they do without Peter their leader, so brave and bold? They could not rescue him, for none could get into the prison. Only one thing they *could* do—they could pray to God for help to save Peter from his enemies, and this they did without ceasing.

Peter, in prison, chained to a soldier on either hand, waited patiently. He was not afraid. He might, perhaps, have saved himself, but, like Jesus, he would not work a miracle just for his own sake. The last day of the Feast passed, and that night Peter lay sleeping between two soldiers chained on either hand as usual, while two other soldiers guarded the doorway. Although he knew that in the morning Herod intended to bring him out to be put to death, Peter's heart was not full of fear; he was sleeping soundly, between his sleeping guardians.

All at once a light shone in the dark prison. Peter was wakened by a touch, and opening his eyes, he saw an angel bending over him. "Arise up quickly," said the angel, giving him his hand, and as Peter rose his chains fell from him, and he was free. But the sleeping soldiers, all unaware, slept on.

The angel told Peter to dress and to put on his sandals, and Peter did so. Then— "Cast thy cloak about thee and follow me," and through the dark and silent prison Peter followed the shining form of the angel; past the first and second guard of soldiers towards the great iron gate which led out to the streets of the city. No one appeared to notice them, no one stayed them. As they drew near the locked and heavy gate, it opened to them of its own accord, and they passed through into the deserted street. Down the street they walked together, and then, suddenly, Peter was alone. The angel had vanished.

All this time Peter had believed himself to be dreaming. But now, as he breathed the cool night air, and looked up into the starry sky above him, Peter realized that he was not asleep, but that the angel of the Lord had indeed been sent to rescue him. "Now I know of a surety," he said to himself, "that the Lord hath sent His angel, and hath delivered me out of the hand of Herod."

He paused awhile, considering what he should do. It would be unwise to stay in Jerusalem, but he must let the disciples know of his rescue. So he turned his footsteps to the house of Mary, the mother of Mark, where he was

The lady of kindness

The rescue of Peter

sure some of his friends would be gathered to pray for him.

Coming to the gate of the house, Peter knocked, and a maiden named Rhoda came. "Who knocks?" she called, listening at the gate, for she could not see who was standing there.

Peter answered her, but Rhoda, when she heard his voice, was so overcome with joy that she ran to tell the others as fast as she could, forgetting, in her glad surprise, to open the gate for Peter. Rushing in, "Peter stands without," she cried. But they could not believe her. "Thou art mad!" they told her. Rhoda repeated that she was *sure* it was Peter, and then someone said, "It is his angel!" But while they were talking, Peter went on knocking, so at last they all went out to the gate and, to their great surprise and joy, found that it was indeed Peter who stood there. They greeted him with cries of delight, and Peter entered the house with them.

Holding up his hand, he asked for quiet while he told them the way of his rescue, and when he had finished his story he directed them to tell the rest of the disciples of his escape. Then he took his leave of them and went away to some quiet haven out of the reach of Herod, the king.

*

Jesus had once said to Peter, "Thou art Peter," —which means "a rock"—"and on this rock will I build my church."

For many troubled years Peter was the leader of the followers of Christ, or Christians, as they came to be called. He gave them faithful help and council, loved them dearly, and taught the Gospel wherever he went, doing loyal work for his master here on earth. We do not read much more of Peter in the Bible, except for two long letters which he wrote to his fellow Christians for their guidance, but we know that at some time he went to Rome, and that there he suffered death for his Master's sake. So that good and faithful servant entered into the joy of his Lord.

PAUL THE TRAVELLER

A Boy in Tarsus

About the time when Jesus was growing up in Nazareth, among the hills of Galilee, another boy was growing up in a city called Tarsus. Tarsus was a Greek city in a country called Cilicia—a city of fine houses and marble temples, with a river of clear water running through it, and a beautiful harbour where proud ships came gliding in from the sea, to furl their sails and ride at anchor, bringing goods and travellers from countries far away; a city where trade caravans filed out through the gates, to cross the mountains towering up beyond the walls—a busy city of many comings and goings.

The boy who was brought up in Tarsus was named Saul. His parents were Jews, strict Pharisees, who kept very carefully all the laws of Moses—all those rules of behaviour and outward observances which they thought

God desired of men. Saul himself, a keen and clever scholar, was sent to school to learn all about the law. At home and at school Saul spoke the Hebrew language, but the people of Tarsus spoke Greek, and Saul could also read and speak Greek, and no doubt he sometimes attended the lectures in the fine university of Tarsus.

One great and much coveted privilege the boy's parents, and Saul himself, possessed—they were Roman citizens. This meant that they could never be scourged or crucified, and that if any dispute arose, they had the right to appeal to Caesar.

Besides going to school and university, Saul was taught a trade. Every Jewish boy was trained to some trade, and Saul was taught to make tents, to weave tough fabric of goats' hair, called cilicium, for which Tarsus was famous.

Saul must often have watched the caravans file out through the gates of the city, or stood on the quay and watched the tall ships sail out into the sunset. Did he wonder to what far lands they were going, and whether he would ever sail away to see them for himself? When he grew up Saul was destined to become one of the most famous travellers of all times.

The Great Awakening

When Saul was a young man he was sent to Jerusalem to study the law under the Rabbi Gamaliel. Here he met some of the followers of Christ, men who claimed that Jesus, Who had suffered the disgraceful death of crucifixion, was really the Saviour, that Messiah whom the Jews had been expecting for so long. Saul was shocked and horrified. The Jews believed that any man crucified was outcast from God. How could such a man be their long-awaited king? Moreover, the disciples taught that Jesus had risen from the dead, and they believed that He was now at the right hand of God in heaven. Saul thought all this terribly wrong and blasphemous, and that people who taught such things should be punished severely, or even destroyed.

When Stephen was stoned to death, Saul was present. He did not actually stone Stephen himself, but he stood there guarding the clothes of the men who did so, as much the murderer of Stephen as those men, for he was glad in his heart to see him die.

After this, Saul was the most ardent of the persecutors of the disciples in Jerusalem. He dragged men and women from their homes, and cast them into prison. He was such a bitter enemy that many of them fled far away. But wherever they went they taught the Gospel of the Lord Jesus, and so the work of Christ went on.

But Saul was to learn how dreadfully mistaken he had been, for God had a plan for him. Saul was to become the "Great Apostle", the bearer of Christ's message to Gentiles, kings and the Children of Israel in far places of the world.

One day Saul, with some companions, started on a journey to Damascus. Saul had heard that there were disciples of Jesus in that city, and he obtained letters from the High Priest to the synagogues, so that if he found there any of the new faith, he might bring them back prisoners to Jerusalem. Eager to do, as he thought, his duty to God, Saul in his zeal hastened along, and at last the travellers saw in the distance the white-walled city lying below them framed in green fields and leafy trees. They were near their journey's end.

Suddenly, as they went, a wonderful light shone round about them—a light brighter even than the burning sun, a light so fiercely strong, that as Saul looked up, his eyes

were blinded, and he fell to the ground. And as he lay there, trembling and afraid, he heard a voice speaking to him.

"Saul, Saul, why persecutest thou Me?"

"Who art thou, Lord?" Saul asked humbly.

"I am Jesus, Whom thou persecutest."

It was Jesus Himself speaking to Saul, and as he listened, Saul knew at last that Jesus had indeed risen from the dead, and was alive for evermore; knew that Peter and

John and Stephen had been right, and that Jesus was truly the Son of God.

Trembling and astonished, he whispered: "Lord, what wouldst Thou have me to do?"

Jesus instructed him to go on into the city, and there he would be told what he must do.

All this time Saul's companions had stood silent and wondering, for they had heard a voice, but had seen no man, and when at last Saul rose from the earth, they discovered that he was blind. They took him gently by the hand and led him to Damascus, to the house of a man named Judas. There he stayed for three days, blind and sorrowful, neither eating nor drinking.

During those days in silence and darkness, Saul prayed for forgiveness with a humble heart, and during this time it was as though the eyes of his *mind* were opened, and he knew the truth at last. Now he had no doubt that Jesus, Whom he had despised, was the Messiah, the Son of God. Now, remembering with shame the stoning of Stephen, he began to understand why Stephen had died so bravely, so serenely, praying for his enemies. For faith in Christ Jesus brought hope, love and joy to all His disciples, and now that faith was Saul's and he longed with all his heart to serve the Lord himself.

Among the disciples in Damascus was a good man named Ananias, and Ananias, like the apostles, had the gift of healing in the name of Jesus. One day Ananias heard God in a vision telling him to seek out Saul of Tarsus, who was living in the city in the Street called Straight, that he might heal him of his blindness.

Now Ananias was quite aware of the cruelty Saul had shown to the Christians in Jerusalem, and he knew why Saul had come to Damascus. So he was astonished, and he could not help protesting a little. Saul had come intending to take him prisoner; was it safe to go and help him?

But the Lord answered: "Go thy way, for I have chosen him to bear My Name before the Gentiles and kings and the Children of Israel." And God told Ananias that Saul was now a servant of Christ, and in the years to come would suffer much for His Name's sake. So Ananias went obediently to find the man who had come as his enemy.

So it came about that Saul, sitting alone in his blindness, heard someone come into the room, felt kind hands upon him, and heard a quiet voice say: "Brother Saul, the Lord, even Jesus, that appeared unto thee in the way as thou camest, hath sent me, that thou mightest receive thy sight, and be filled with the Holy Spirit."

And straightway Saul's eyes were opened, and he could

137

see again. He stood up and thanked his kind friend, and Ananias baptised him, and the Holy Spirit was given to *him*, as it was to those others who had faith in Christ Jesus.

Then Saul was given food and drink, and strength came back to him. Ananias took him to meet the other disciples in Damascus, and they received him with friendship and goodwill, and soon this man, who had come as an enemy, was one of the best beloved among the little company of Christians, and he taught Christ Jesus in the synagogues of the city.

In Peril by the Heathen

There came a time, however, when God called Saul, or Paul, for now he used the Greek form of his name, to go on many long and dangerous journeys to preach the Gospel in far lands. God had told Ananias that Paul would suffer much for His Name's sake, and during those years of his travelling Paul bravely endured hardships, poverty, hunger and thirst; he was beaten, he was stoned, he was imprisoned, he was shipwrecked. Paul himself once wrote that he went "in journeyings often, in perils of waters, in perils of robbers, in perils of mine own countrymen, in perils by the heathen, in perils in the city, in perils in the wilderness, in perils in the sea". Yet his courage never failed; he ceased not to preach Christ Jesus wherever he went.

The history of Paul's journeys is as thrilling and exciting as any adventure story ever written, and whenever he left a town or city, he left behind him a firmly established church for Christ, and many loyal friends for himself.

Whenever Paul first visited any city, he went first of all to the synagogue, there to preach the wonderful story of the death and resurrection of Jesus to his own people, the Jews. Some of them would listen willingly, and believe; but many only scorned and hated him and his message. Then Paul would carry the good news to the Gentiles, teaching them that God was *their* Father, too, and Christ their Saviour. "Gentiles" was the name given by the Jews to all people who did not belong to the Jewish race. Paul's preaching to the Gentiles always infuriated the unbelieving Jews. They refused to acknowledge Jesus themselves, and they could not bear that others should serve Him as Lord and King. This jealous ill-will made things very difficult for Paul, for these Jews who hated him followed him from city to city, stirring up the people against him, so

that often his work was hindered, and he went in danger of his life.

At one time Paul and Barnabas had been driven from Antioch and Iconium by their enemies, and had arrived in a little town called Lystra. Here the heathen people listened quietly to Paul, and when Paul, in the name of Jesus, cured a poor man, a cripple, who had never been able to walk, they were so amazed by the miracle they thought their gods had come to visit them in the likeness of men. Their priests brought garlanded oxen to sacrifice to the apostles, and the people followed in a great procession, ready to worship them.

Paul and Barnabas, horrified, had great difficulty in persuading the people to stop the ceremony, and to believe that they, the apostles, were only men like themselves, come to bring them news of the one true God, and of His Son Jesus Christ.

The heathen people were very disappointed, and when some of the enemy Jews arrived and began to speak evil of Paul and Barnabas, they became angry too.

They stoned poor Paul, and left him for dead outside the gates of the town. But fortunately Paul was not really dead. Barnabas, and the faithful friends they had made in Lystra, were able after a time to revive him with wine, and to bathe his wounds. They tended him with loving care until he regained a little strength, and that night he rested in the home of one of their new friends. The next day Barnabas took him away to a city called Derbe.

But soon, with invincible courage, Paul and Barnabas were returning through Lystra, Iconium and Antioch, to help and encourage the new disciples who had been brave enough to turn to Christ Jesus.

In Peril in Philippi

It was midnight in the prison of Philippi. In the cold, dark cells the prisoners huddled wretchedly. In the darkest, dreariest dungeon of all sat two men, their feet fast in the stocks, their clothes torn, their bare backs raw and bleeding from terrible beatings.

Suddenly, in the darkness, someone began to pray aloud, and then two deep, musical voices rang out in a joyful hymn of praise to God.

The other prisoners listened in wonder. They knew that the singers were the two Jewish prisoners locked in the innermost dungeon. How *could* they sound so joyful—bound with chains, burning with the pain of their wounds? Why were they not groaning in misery?

On the day before, Paul and his companion Silas—for they were the singing prisoners—had preached Christ Jesus in the streets of Philippi, and Paul had cast out an evil spirit from a poor slave girl who had followed them. But this had greatly angered the poor girl's masters, for they made much money by her fortune-telling. Now she would

be of no more use to them. Furious with rage, these wicked men rushed upon Paul and Silas and dragged them to the marketplace, and took them before the Roman magistrates. To the magistrates, and the people, they told, not

143

the *real* reason of their complaint against Paul, but *lies* that he and Silas were working against the Roman power.

The magistrates, not even trying to find out the truth, ordered Paul and Silas to be cruelly beaten and thrust into prison, and the jailer was told to keep them safely, or he would pay with his life. Paul and Silas had borne all this injustice patiently, and now in the cold and darkness, in pain and discomfort, they sang of their love and faith in God.

All at once, drowning the singing voices, a deep, frightening rumble was heard. Among cries of panic the whole building shook; doors were wrenched open, chains rattled as the staples in the walls to which they were fastened fell out, and in the noise, dust and confusion of that terrible earthquake, the prisoners realized that they were free.

The jailer, awakened from sleep by the frightful noise, sprang up with a cry, and seeing that all the doors were opened, he thought the prisoners had escaped. With a groan of despair he drew his sword, meaning to kill himself. But out from the darkness and confusion Paul's voice cried to him loudly: "Do thyself no harm, for we are all here!"

What a relief to the jailer! Sheathing his sword, he called for a light, and running in to Paul and Silas, he fell at their feet, trembling with fear. But they spoke reassur-

The Roman soldiers take Paul by night from Jerusalem

Paul tells his fellow passengers of his vision

ing words to him, and as the earthquake died away, he drew them out of the dungeon, and asked humbly: "Sirs, what must I do to be saved?" The apostles answered: "Believe in the Lord Jesus Christ, and thou shalt be saved," and there, in the prison, to that Roman soldier, they taught the Word of the Lord, and before morning dawned the jailer and all his house had become Christians, and were baptised.

The apostles' wounds were bathed and anointed, the jailer provided them with refreshing food and drink at his own house, and for the rest of that night they rested comfortably there.

In the early morning came a message from the frightened magistrates. Alarmed by the dreadful earthquake, and knowing they had done wrong to imprison men without a trial, they sent word to the jailer: "Let these men go."

How joyfully the jailer carried the news to Paul and Silas! "Now therefore depart," he told them, "and go in peace."

But Paul would not. He and Silas were Roman citizens. The magistrates had done very wrong in ordering them to be beaten and imprisoned without a proper trial, and if it were known to the Roman authorities, they would get into grave trouble. They should not now send them away secretly as though they were really guilty men. The city must know that the followers of Christ were not law-breakers. So Paul sent a message to say that the magistrates must come themselves to set them free.

The magistrates were very much afraid when they knew that Paul and Silas were Roman citizens. They came hurrying at once to ask their pardon, and to beg them to depart from the city.

Paul and Silas walked out of the prison and went straight to the house of a kind lady named Lydia, who had befriended them before, and there they met, and spoke comforting words to, the Christians of Philippi ere they set out on their travels once more.

Preaching in Athens

After many troubles and difficulties Paul at last reached Athens, the capital of Greece and the most beautiful city in the world of its time. Paul had proclaimed Jesus Christ as King to many different kinds of people, but now he was to learn how the wisest and most cultured and artistic people would receive his message.

Paul was guided to Athens by some friends who had to leave him there, so as he wandered about the city he must have felt lonely in the midst of all these strangers. Everywhere, as he looked about him, he saw wonderful statues of gods and goddesses, carved in snow-white marble. There were so many that the people would joke and say it was easier to find a god than a man in Athens. And everywhere around the city also were the exquisitely built temples of the gods, with finely carved pillars of white and coloured marble, ornamental pavements, and walls adorned with wonderful paintings.

In that bright, sunny atmosphere all the city seemed full of loveliness and the scent of flowers, and as Paul wandered up the heights he could gaze out upon the full glory of the blue sky and the blue sea, the sunlit islands, the ships, the birds, and in the distance the high mountain peaks.

Athens was indeed like a queen of wonder, for the Athenians were the greatest artists in the world. Even today, no one can carve such marvellous statues as the Athenians carved, and modern nations are proud to have even broken pieces of these statues in their museums for us to look at.

But Paul could not find any real pleasure in what he

saw around him, but he remembered that the people were idle and wicked, and either worshipped their foolish gods or else worshipped their own wisdom. His keen spirit longed to show them the glory of Jesus Christ, and he soon found his way to the synagogue to begin his work by talking to the Jews before going to the marketplace to talk to the Athenians themselves.

Even the marketplace was beautiful with paintings. Here one could buy food, cattle and horses, and beautiful clothes and wonderful treasures which had come from all over the world. There was even one part where slaves could be bought.

So day after day Paul sat there with a little crowd of people listening to him, either out of idle curiosity or with genuine interest, as he told the strange story of a God who had come down to earth not as a great prince or as a mighty warrior, but as a simple person, to be despised and scourged, and spat upon, and crucified.

But this was not all Paul's message—Jesus Christ had risen from the dead, so he cried out, and was even then standing at the right hand of God. The crowds increased, and the Athenians began to argue with each other as to what this stranger meant. At last some of the most learned men of the city invited him to come before their council on a hill called Areopagus and explain to them this new religion.

This was a great honour for Paul, according to the Athenians. He had to ascend a long flight of steps, and at the top he found the chief Athenians seated. Paul himself stood on a block of stone, and the people crowded up the steps and sat as close as they could so that they might hear what he had to say, for the Athenians liked nothing better than to tell or hear of some new thing.

From where Paul stood he could see below him the idol temples, the altars, the shrines and the statues, and his heart yearned that some words of his might lead these Athenians to know the true God. So he told them a story of how, as he passed through their city, he had seen an altar bearing the inscription "To the Unknown God". He explained to the Athenians that he knew they were very religious—so religious, indeed, that in order to be quite sure that no god had been left out, they had put up this altar.

Paul ended his story by telling the Athenians that the Unknown God whom they were ignorantly worshipping, was in truth the very God about whom he was preaching. Looking down on the temples, he cried out: "God that made the world, and all things therein, seeing that He is Lord of heaven and earth, dwelleth not in temples made with hands, neither is worshipped with men's hands, as though He needed anything, seeing He giveth to all life and breadth and all things.

Then Paul went on to tell them that they must not think that God was made of gold and silver, or of beautifully carved stone, for the true God, whom we cannot see, is the Father of us all.

At first the Athenians listened carefully to what Paul said, but as soon as he began to speak about Jesus Christ having risen from the dead, these wise people began to mock, and to laugh and to scorn Paul, while some, rather more politely, said they would come and hear about it another day.

Paul was deeply disappointed, for he knew that no one who mocked Jesus would ever be a Christian. He never spoke to these people again, so they missed their chance. Today there are millions of Christians all over the world, but the gods and the temples of the Athenians are mostly broken in pieces.

In Peril in Ephesus

One lovely spring day in May, Paul came to the city of Ephesus, where he was to live for some two years. The people there had never heard of Jesus Christ, the wonderful teacher and healer. Instead they worshipped a very large silver idol, which they called Diana. Paul went here and there in Ephesus, talking to groups of people whenever they would listen, telling them of Jesus and his love.

Living at Ephesus was a man called Demetrius. He had a large workshop, and with the help of his workmen he made little silver statues of Diana, which he sold to visitors. This had made him a very rich man, so he was very annoyed when he heard that Paul had come to Ephesus and was telling the people about Jesus.

He called his workmen together, and told them how Paul was preaching in the streets of Ephesus and telling the people of a great King called Jesus, and how already many people were turning away from worshipping Diana, and how this would affect them. "Sirs," he said, "ye know that by this craft we have our wealth."

The men, who earned their living by this work, were very angry. They rushed into the street shouting, "Great is Diana of the Ephesians," and other people joined in. When the workmen saw two friends of Paul, Gaius and Aristarchus, they seized them and took them to the great open-air theatre. Paul tried to come to the aid of his friends, but they sent a message to him, pleading with him not to come. And indeed, if Paul had been with them the angry mob would probably have stoned him to death.

It was a long time before the shouting died down, but at last the town clerk spoke to them, telling them that they should be quiet and do nothing rashly, for "If Demetrius and the craftsmen which are with him have a matter against any man, the law is open, and there are deputies. Let them implead one another. But if ye enquire anything concerning other matters, it shall be determined in a lawful assembly."

In little groups the crowd walked away, and soon the theatre was empty. Gaius and Aristarchus were free now to go on helping Paul to spread the good news about Jesus.

In Peril from his Countrymen

It was night. The quiet stars shone down over the dreaming city of Jerusalem. Only in the Roman castle near the Temple were any signs of wakefulness. There, near the barracks, torches flared, there came a jingle of harness—a tramp of feet—sudden words of command, and out through the gates marched a great company of soldiers and spearmen, with seventy troopers on horseback, and in the midst of them all rode a prisoner—Paul. Once more a captive, never to be a free man again, Paul was leaving his beloved Jerusalem for the last time.

Though aware of his danger, Paul had come to attend the Feast of Pentecost, and to see his Christian friends once more. But those same enemies who had hindered his work in other cities made great trouble for him, stirring up the people to anger and rioting. Paul was almost torn in pieces, and so great was the uproar that soldiers had been sent to take him to the castle. There the chief captain, when Paul declared himself a Roman citizen, had treated him well, and when news was brought to him by Paul's own nephew of the Jews' plot to murder his prisoner, the captain decided to send him away secretly.

So there was Paul, riding through the night, away from his friends, away from the beloved city, away from the hate of his countrymen. How sad and lonely he must have felt! But he had one great comfort, for God had spoken to him during the night before: "Be of good cheer, Paul, for as thou hast testified of Me in Jerusalem, so must thou bear witness of Me in Rome." Paul's sore heart took comfort, for he knew God was pleased with the work he had done.

He was escorted by the troopers to Caesarea, and handed over to the Roman Governor, Felix. There he was kept in prison for two years, though his friends were allowed to visit him. Then a new Governor, Festus, came.

Once more the Jews in Jerusalem tried to get Paul into

their power. When Festus visited Jerusalem, they asked that Paul should be sent to them to be tried. But Festus refused. Later, when Paul and his accusers appeared before the Governor in Caesarea, and Festus asked Paul if he were willing to go to Jerusalem to be tried, Paul himself refused, knowing that he would have no fair trial there. Then, as was his right as a Roman citizen, he cried: "I appeal unto Caesar!" This meant that he must go to Rome, there to be tried in the Emperor's court. The Jews were furious, seeing Paul escape them, but Festus put Paul in the charge of a centurion named Julius, and sent him, with some other prisoners, to Rome.

In Peril on the Sea

Paul had been on many dangerous journeys, and three times he had been shipwrecked. He was getting old and tired, not fit now for long and perilous voyages, so with him in the ship went two of his friends, Luke, his beloved doctor, who tells the story, and Aristarchus. They did what they could to look after him, and Julius, the Roman centurion, respected Paul, and treated him well.

Luke's story of this adventurous voyage is most vivid and thrilling. They set sail in a little coasting vessel, in which they travelled—very slowly, for winds were against them—as far as a city called Myra. There they left the little ship, and the centurion, finding a grain ship about to sail for Italy, put his charges aboard her.

It was autumn, and soon it would be dangerous to sail the seas, so the captain and the centurion sought a harbour where they might stay until the spring. They sailed slowly—for the winds were still contrary—towards the island of Crete, and they came first to a place with the happy name of Fair Havens. Paul, who had been on so many voyages, and who knew much about the weather to be expected at sea at that time of the year, urged them to winter in Fair Havens, but the captain persuaded the centurion that it would be wise to find a better harbour. So, on a day when the south wind blew softly, they set sail for Phenice, in western Crete.

But before they could get there a terrible tempest arose. The great ship drifted helplessly before the wind, while towering waves crashed over her. Then, for many days the unfortunate travellers saw neither sun by day, nor stars by night, and when captain and crew, with help from the passengers, had done all they could, throwing overboard everything possible to lighten the ship, and *still* the tempest raged, they gave up all hope of being saved.

Then it was that Paul spoke words of good cheer, telling them all that God, Whom he loved and served, had promised him that, although the ship would be lost, every one of her passengers should be saved, cast up on a certain island.

For fourteen dreadful days and nights they were buffeted and driven up and down in the tumbling waters, and then at last, one pitch-dark night, the sailors suddenly shouted that they thought land was near. How excited everyone was! They stood anxiously by while the shipmen sounded to find the depth of the water—twenty fathoms! A little farther on they sounded again, to find only fifteen fathoms! It was *true*—they were nearing land! But lest they should run on hidden rocks in the darkness, the sailors cast anchors to wait until the morning.

Then once more, while they waited for the longed-for daylight, Paul spoke comforting words to his fellow travellers, telling them again that everyone would be saved, and urging them to eat and drink to keep up their strength. And he took bread, gave thanks to God before them all and began to eat. Everyone was cheered, and ate and drank in good spirits.

When morning dawned at last, they saw land ahead, and with infinite trouble they ran the ship aground, but the heavy waves broke the ship in two, only her fore part sticking fast on the shore.

Then the soldiers wanted to kill the prisoners lest any escape and they themselves get into trouble. But Julius, wishing to save Paul, ordered all who could to swim ashore. The rest also, some on boards, and some on broken pieces of the ship, came safely to land. Not a life was lost.

They found themselves on an island called Melita, which we know as Malta. The people of the island showed them great kindness, kindling a fire for them, giving them food, clothing and shelter.

Paul and the others helped to gather wood for the fire, and as Paul was gathering a bundle of sticks, a deadly poisonous snake fastened on his hand. The islanders, watching, expected to see Paul fall dead at any moment. But Paul just shook the snake off into the fire, and took no hurt. When they saw that the people were so astonished they thought Paul must be a god, and treated him with honour and respect.

Publius, the chief man of the island, lodged Paul and his friends in his own house for three days. There Paul found the father of Publius sick of a fever. Going in to the poor man, Paul prayed, laid his hands on him, and healed him in the Name of Jesus Christ.

When the islanders knew this, many of them brought their sick friends to Paul, and he healed them all. Be sure he also told them of his Lord and Master, Jesus Christ, our Saviour. The rough islanders grew to love Paul well.

When spring came and it was safe to sail away again, their kind hosts loaded them with gifts, sorry to say good-bye, especially to Paul.

And so at last Paul reached Rome, and for the rest of his life he was a prisoner, though allowed to live in his own house and have friends to visit him. He continued to teach the Gospel, and he wrote many wonderful letters, and received news from all the churches he had founded.

But at last Caesar, to whom he had appealed, ordered that he should be killed with the sword. So the great apostle went to his great reward. He had fought a great fight, he had finished his course. But his work goes on, for the story of his dauntless courage, and the wonderful words he wrote, help and inspire men and women to this day.